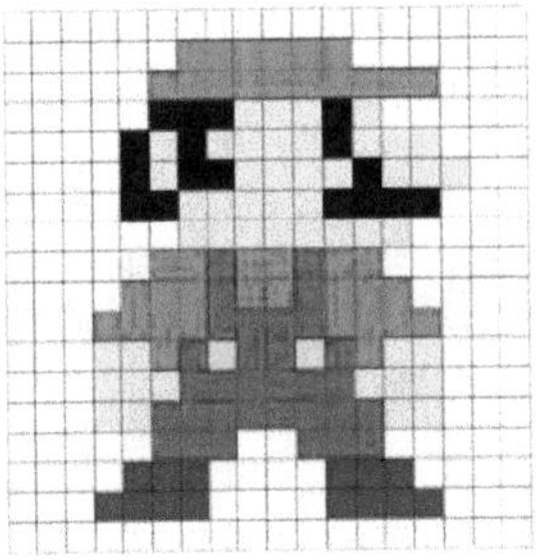

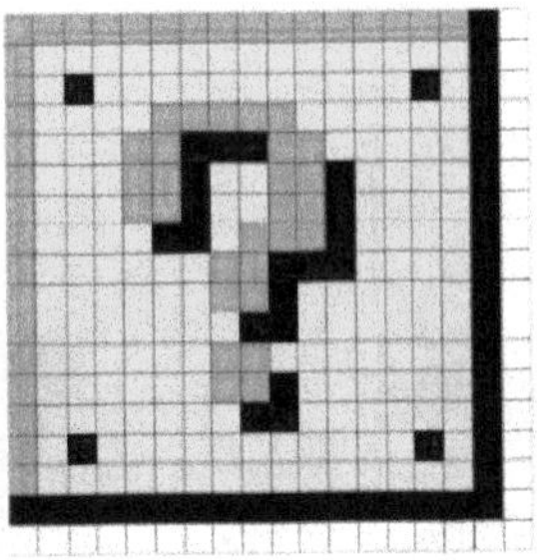

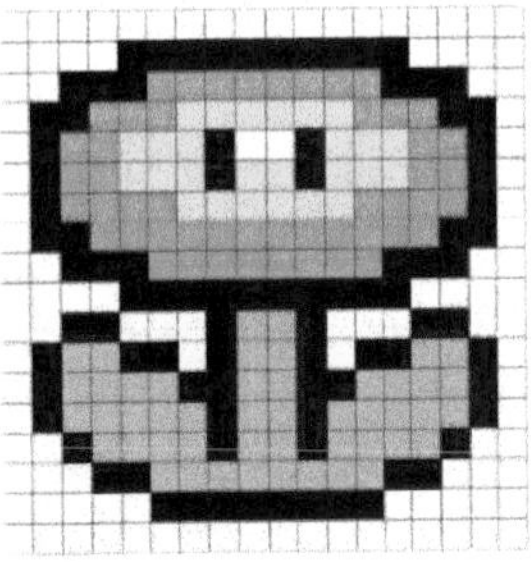

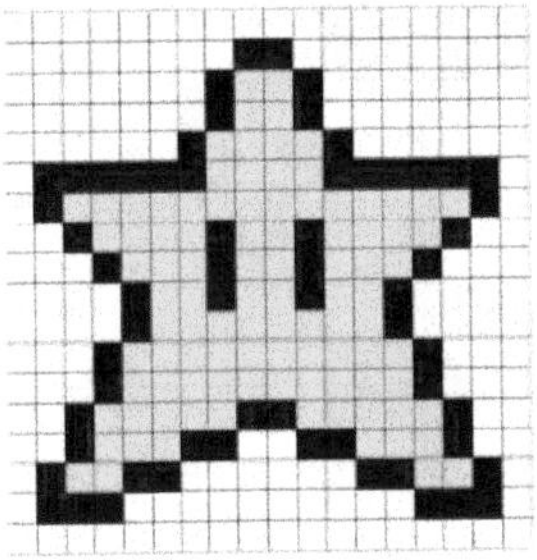

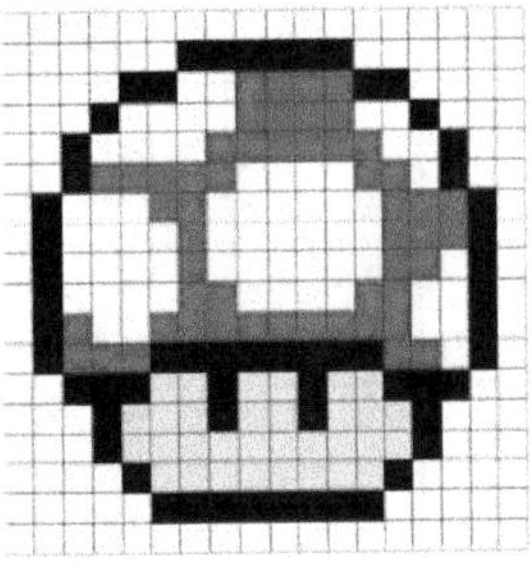

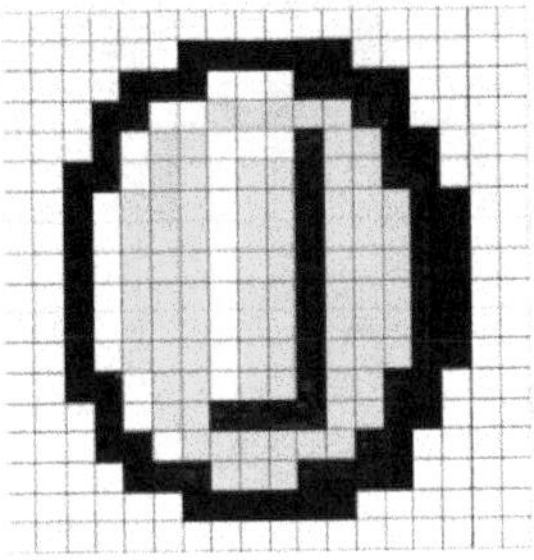

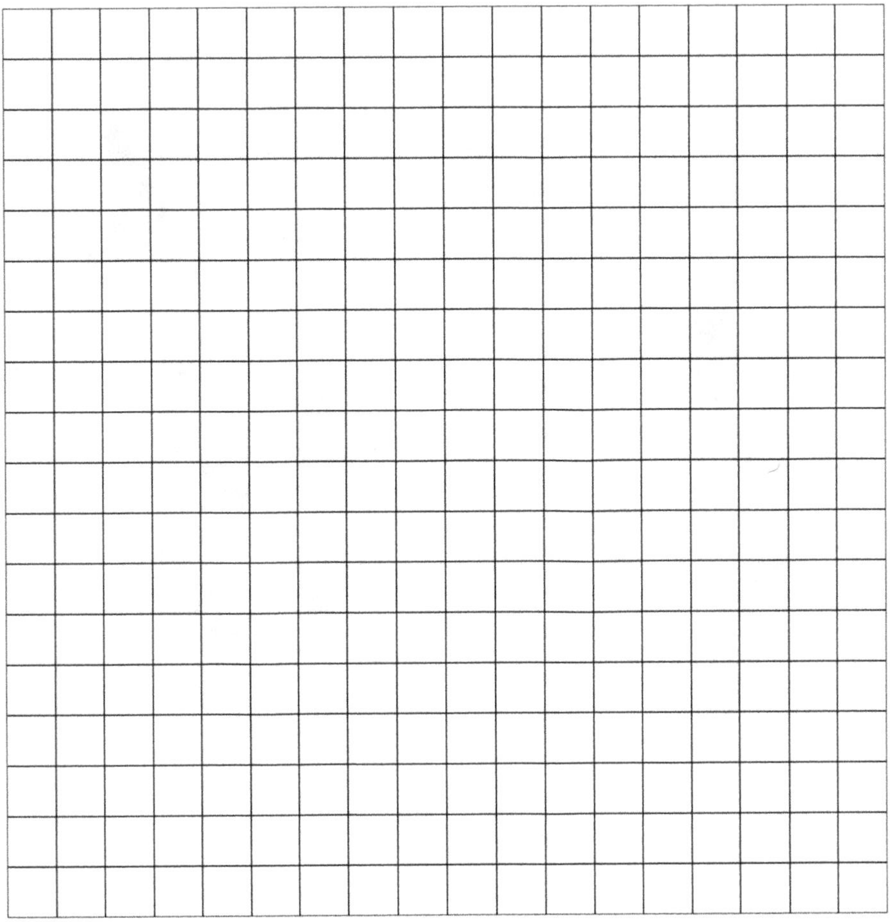

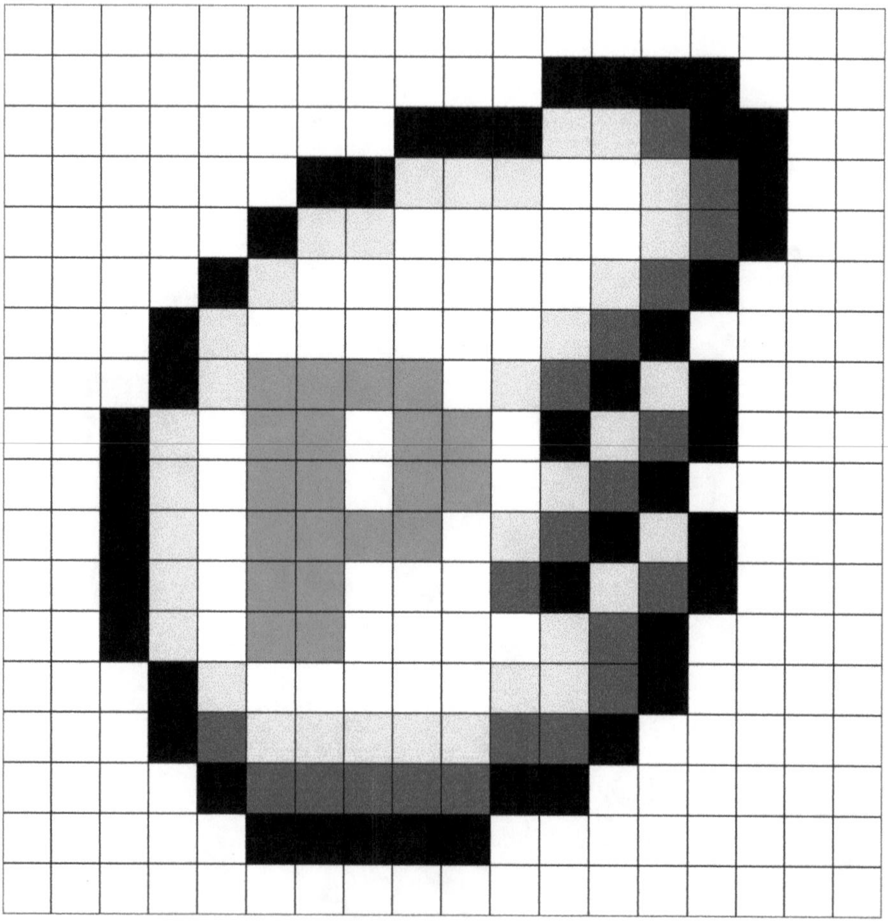

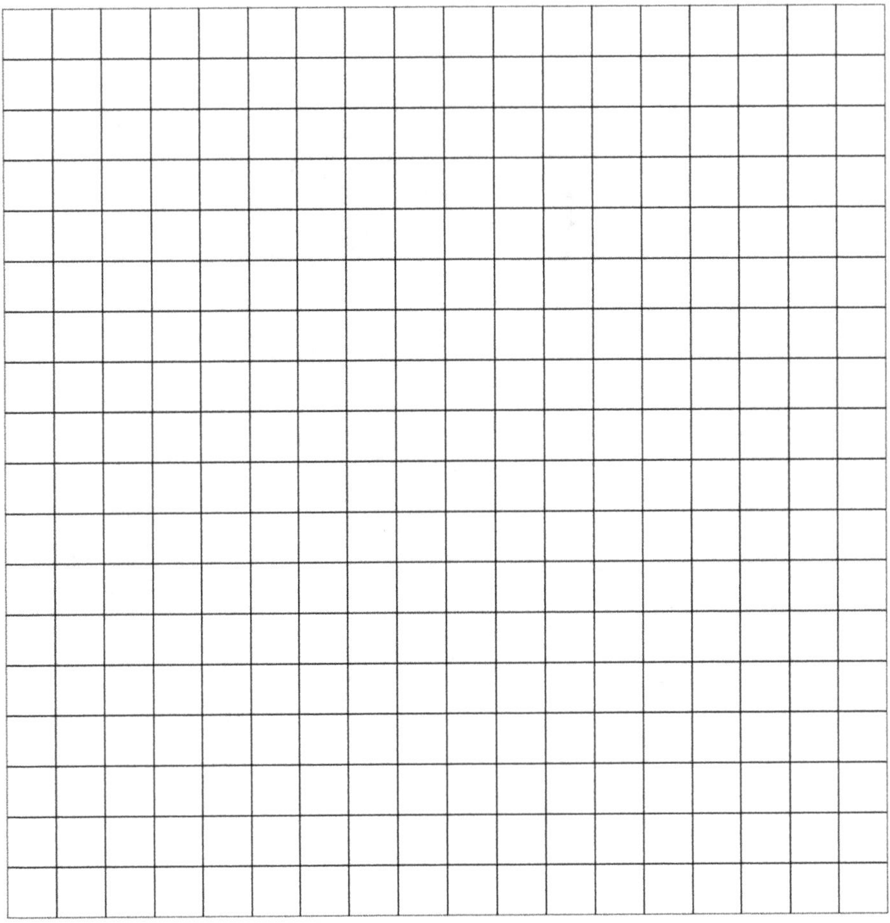

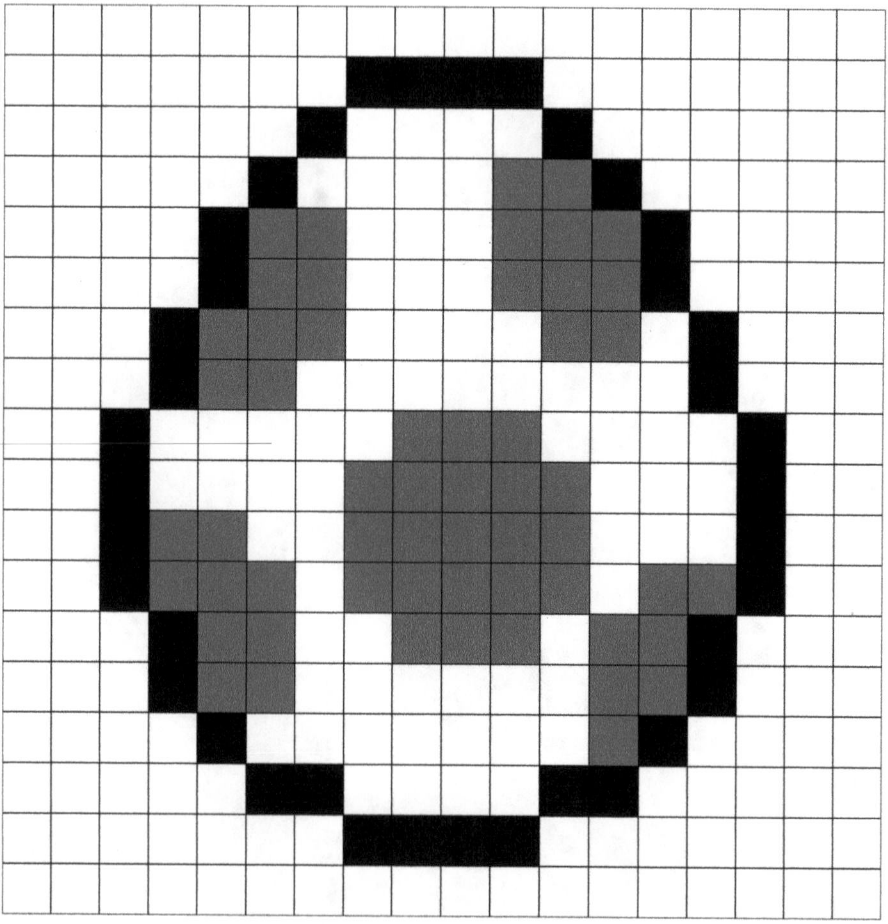

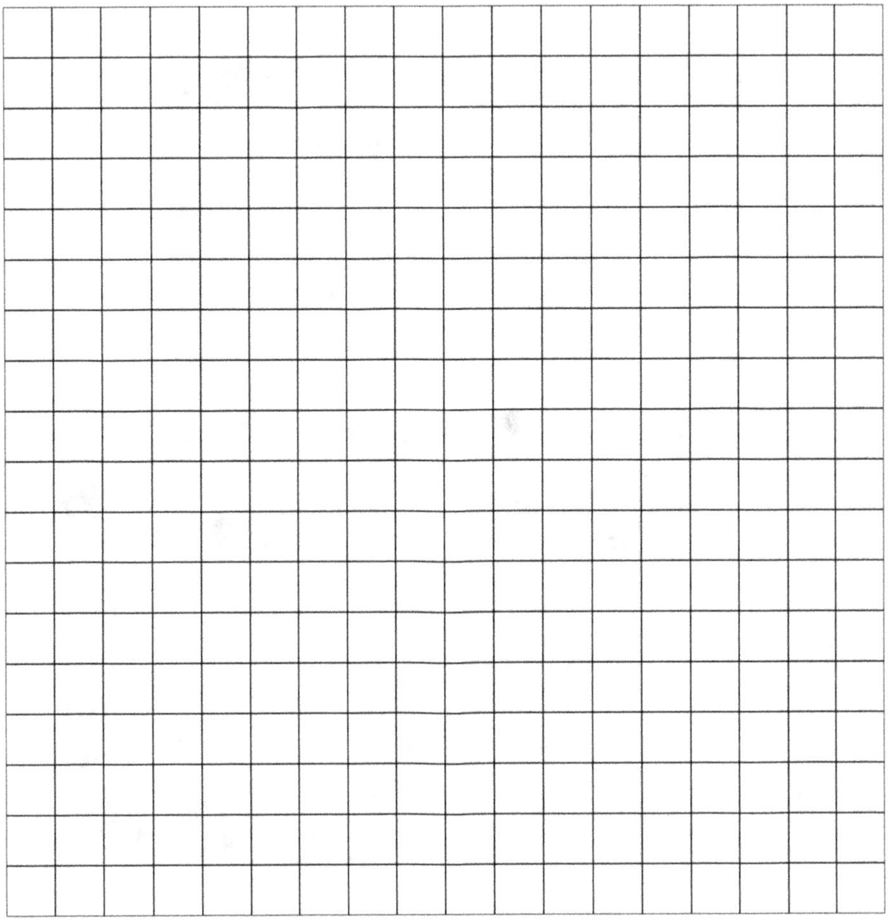

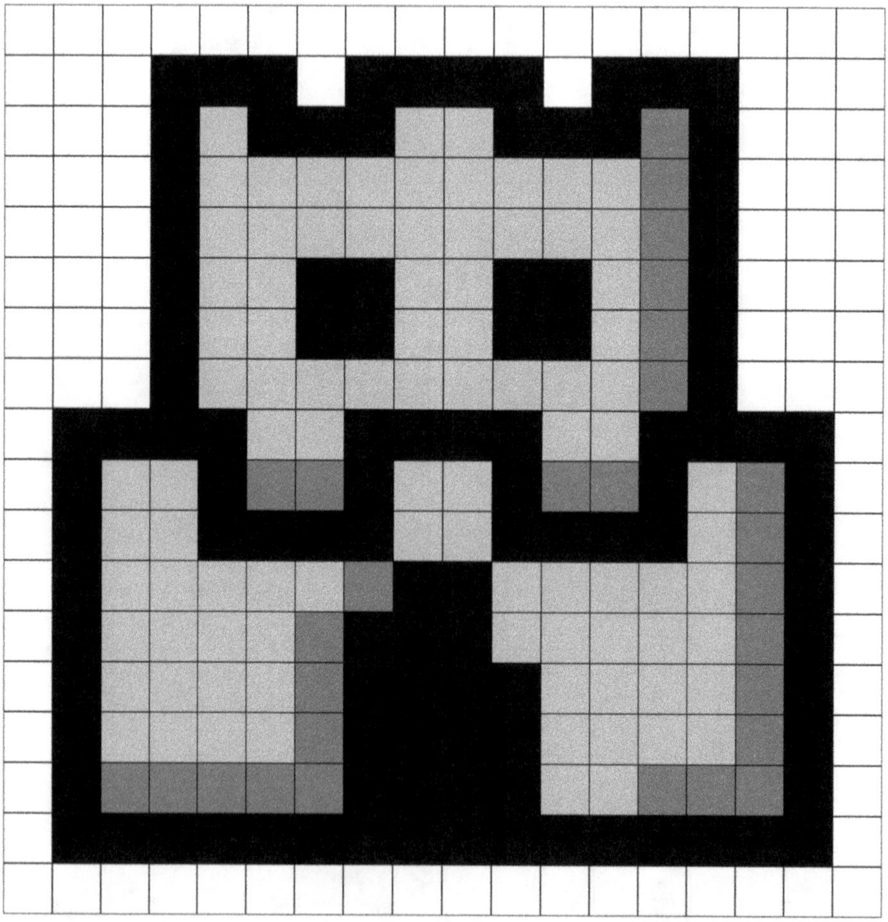

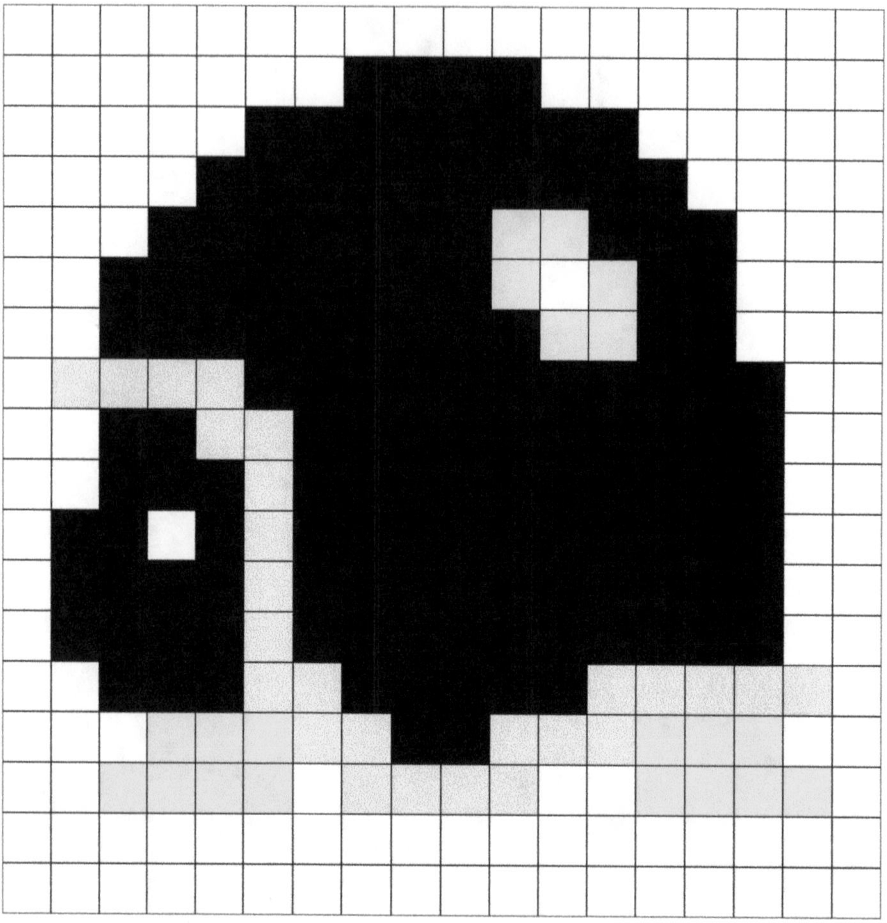

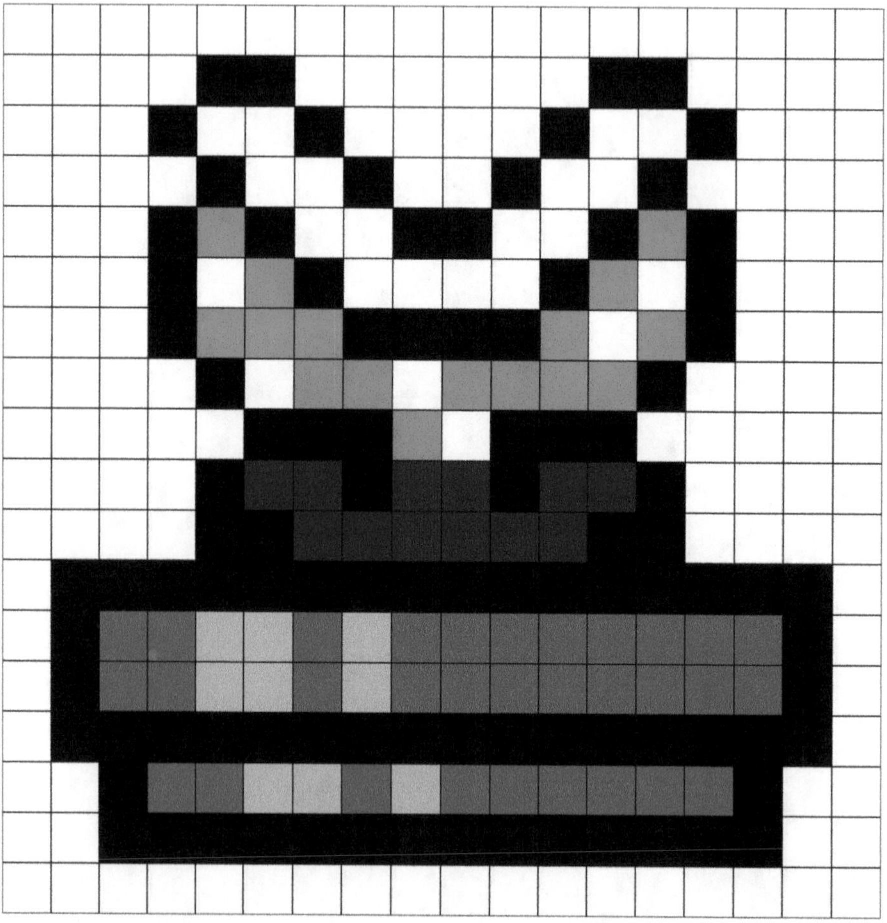

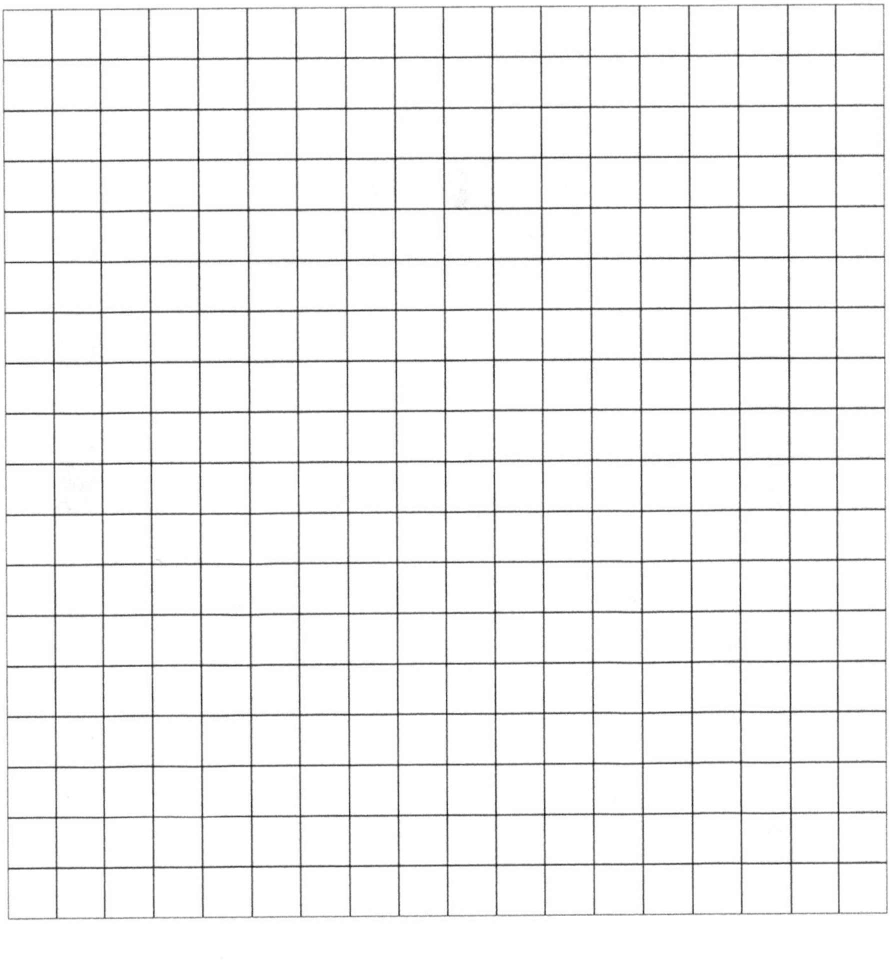

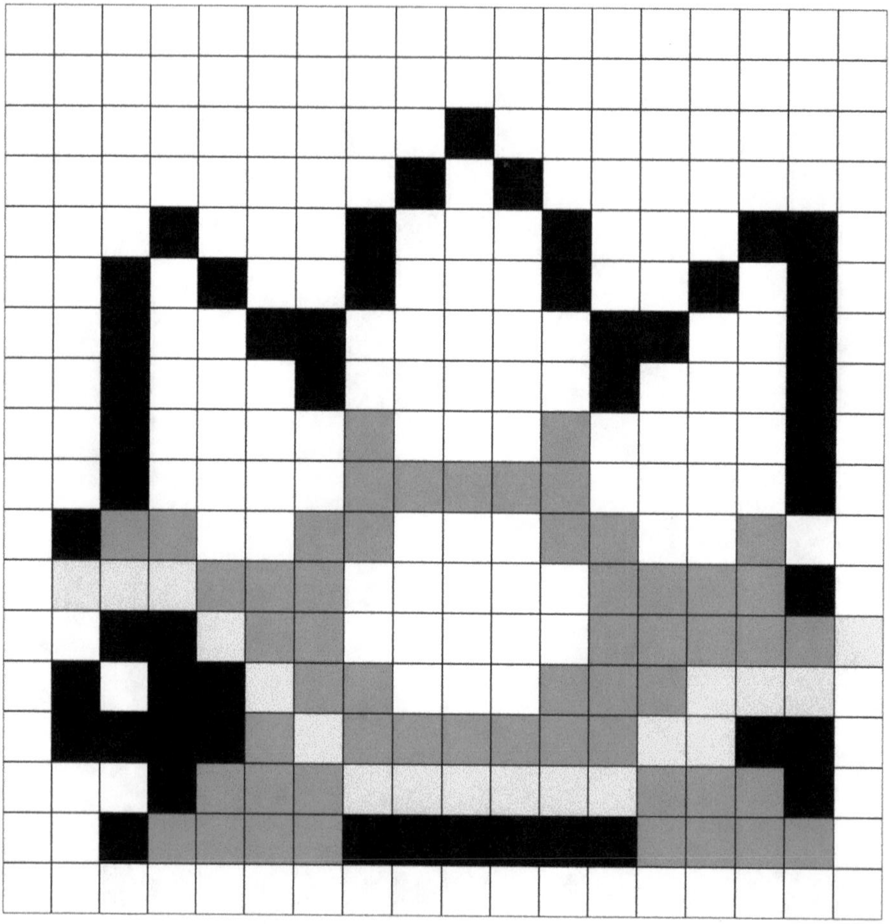

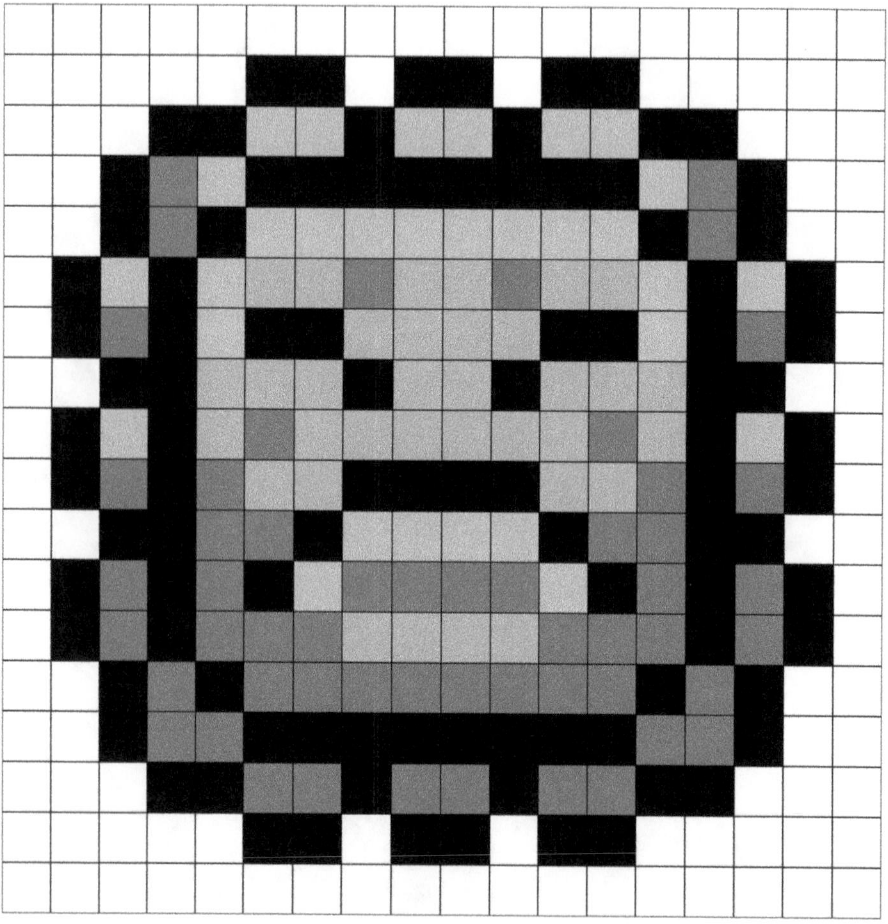

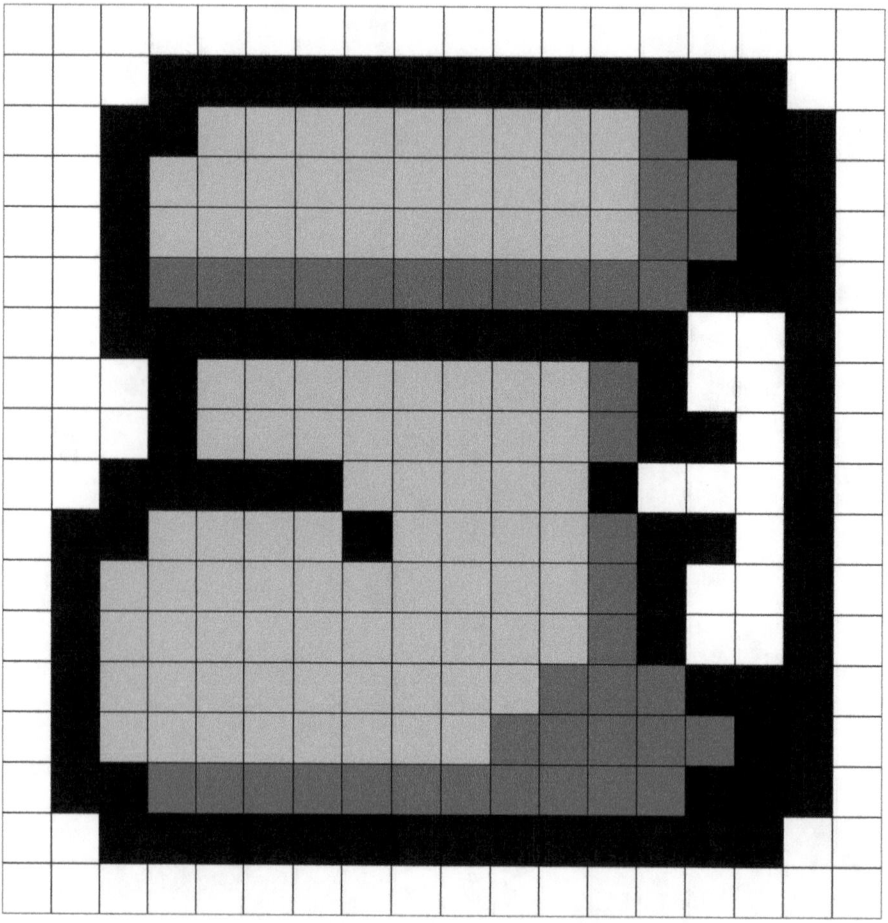

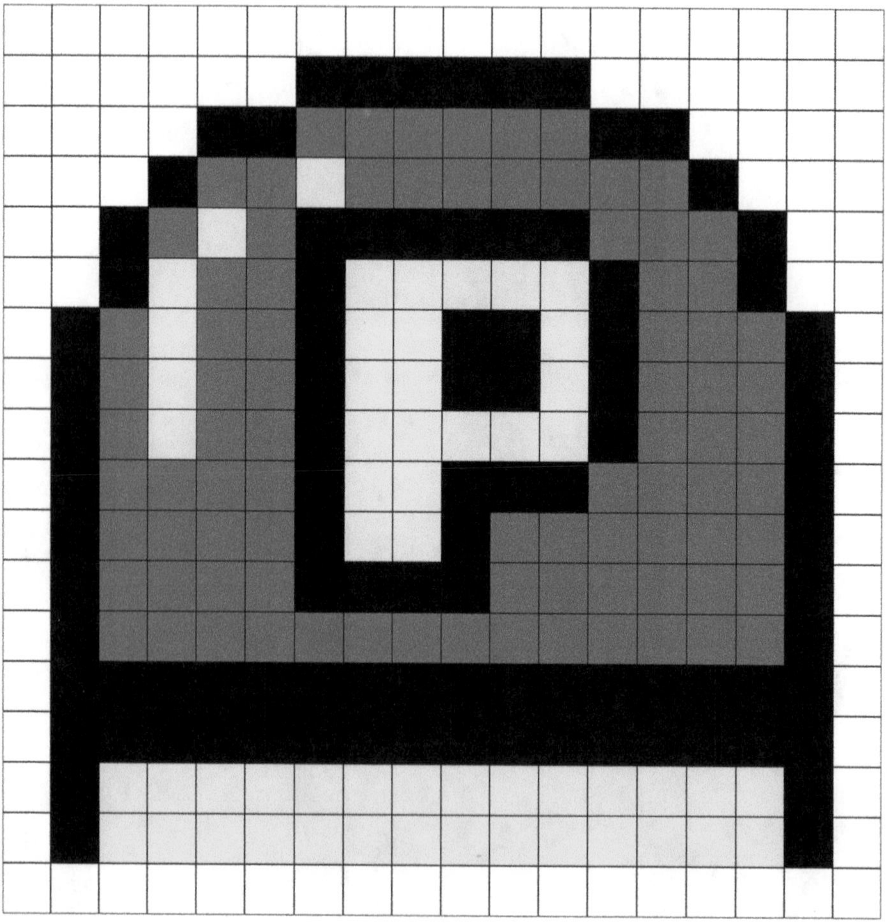

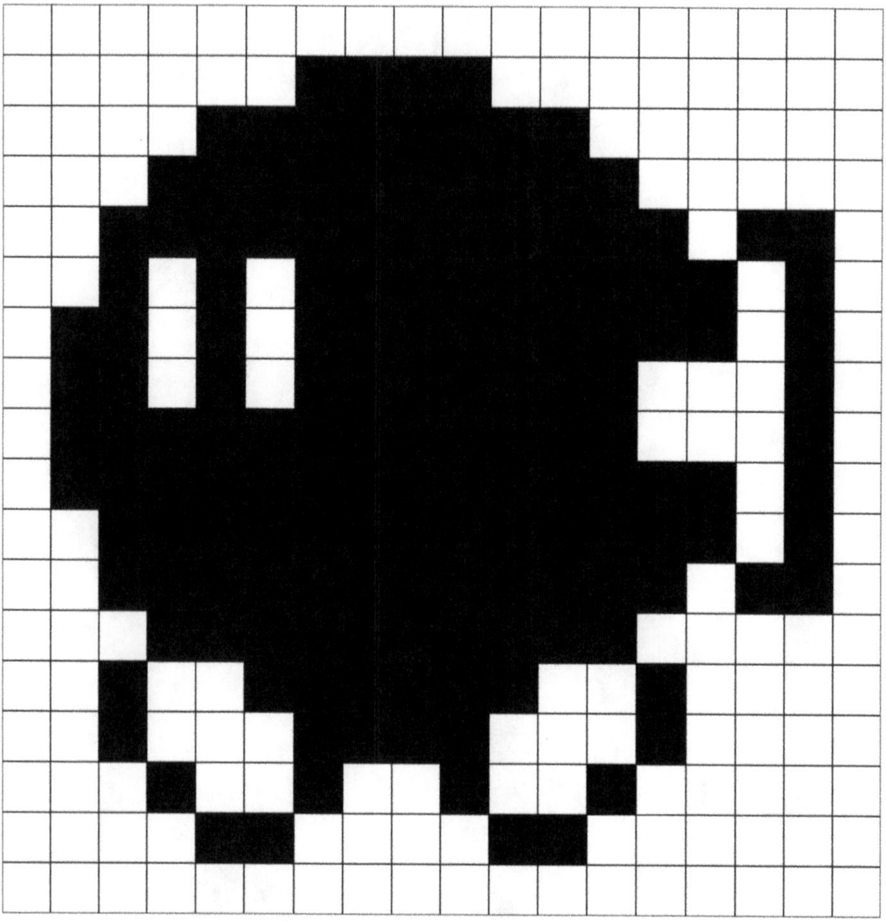

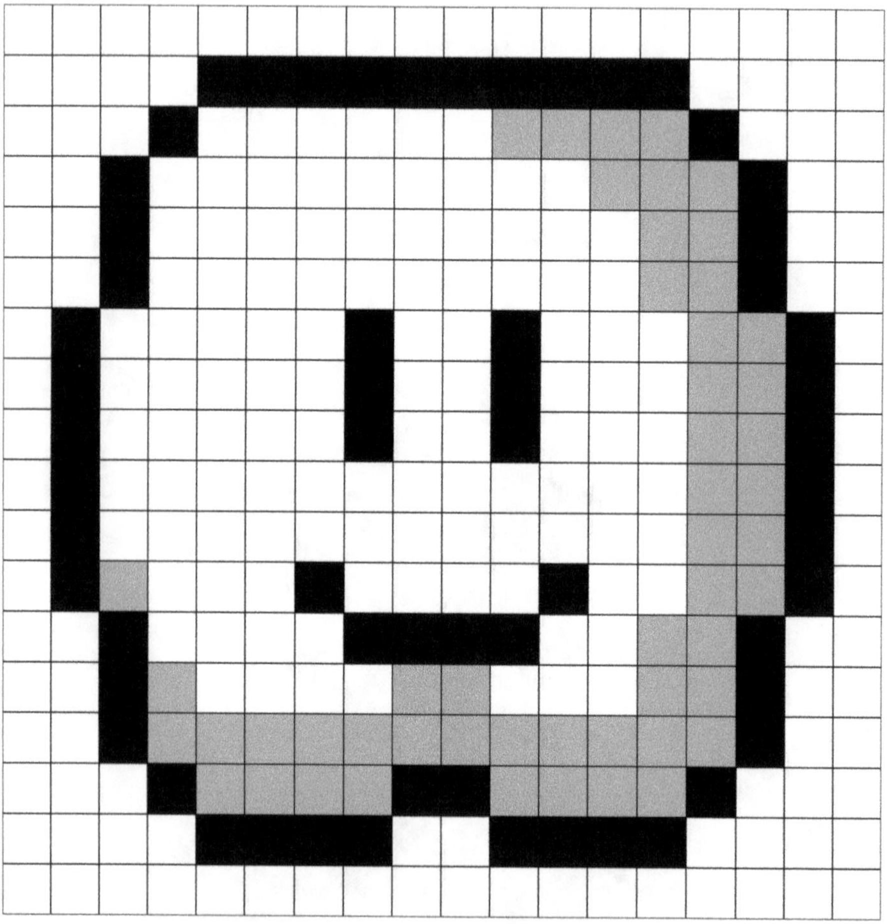

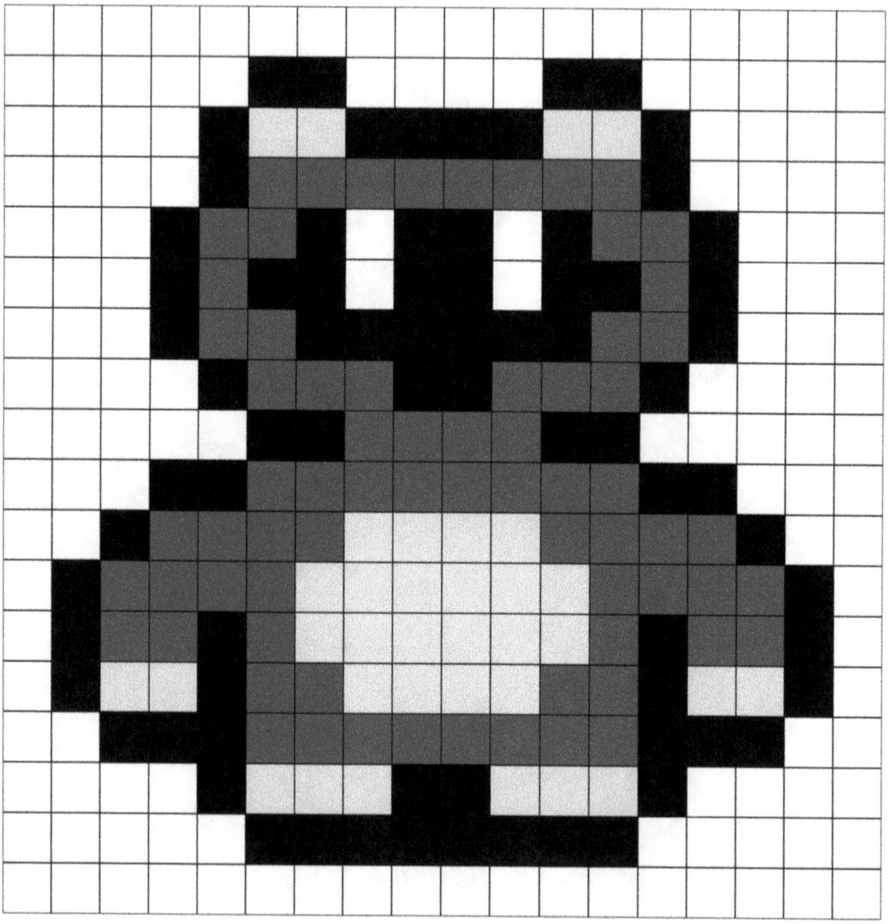

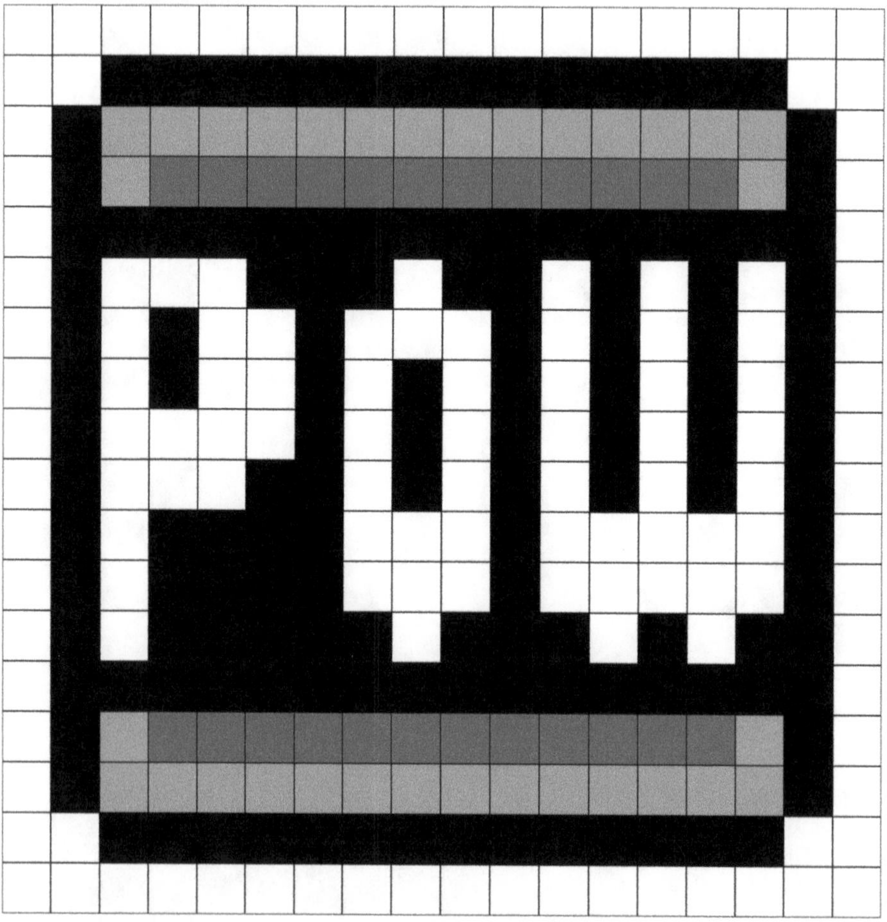
POW

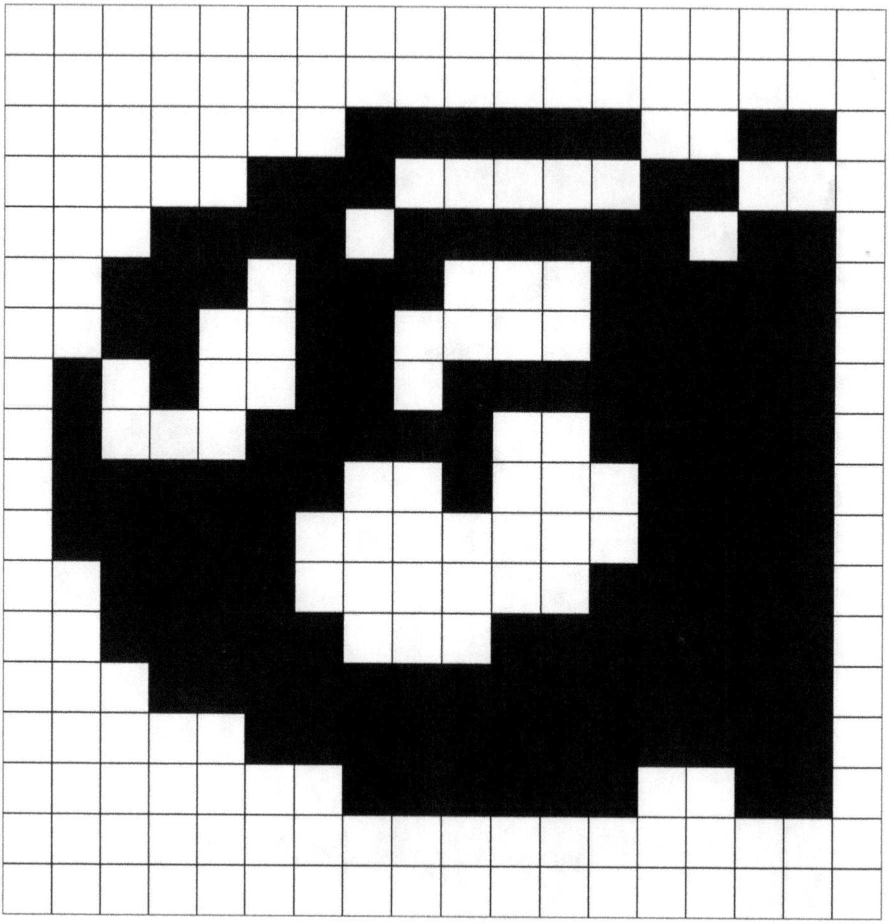

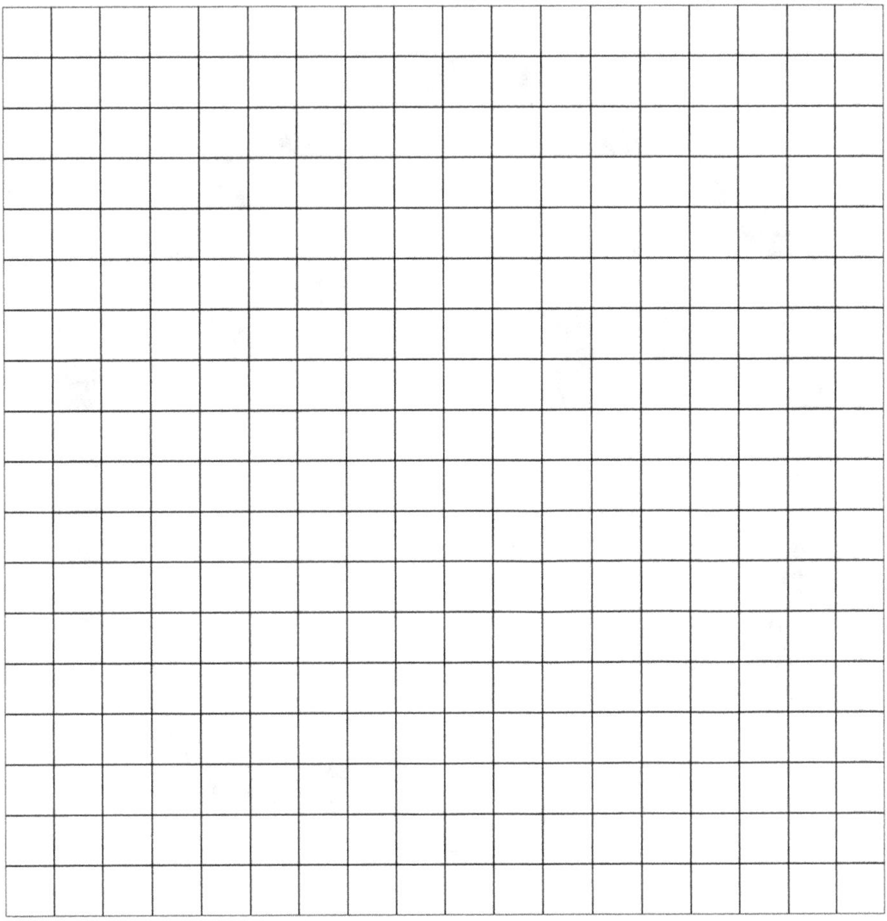

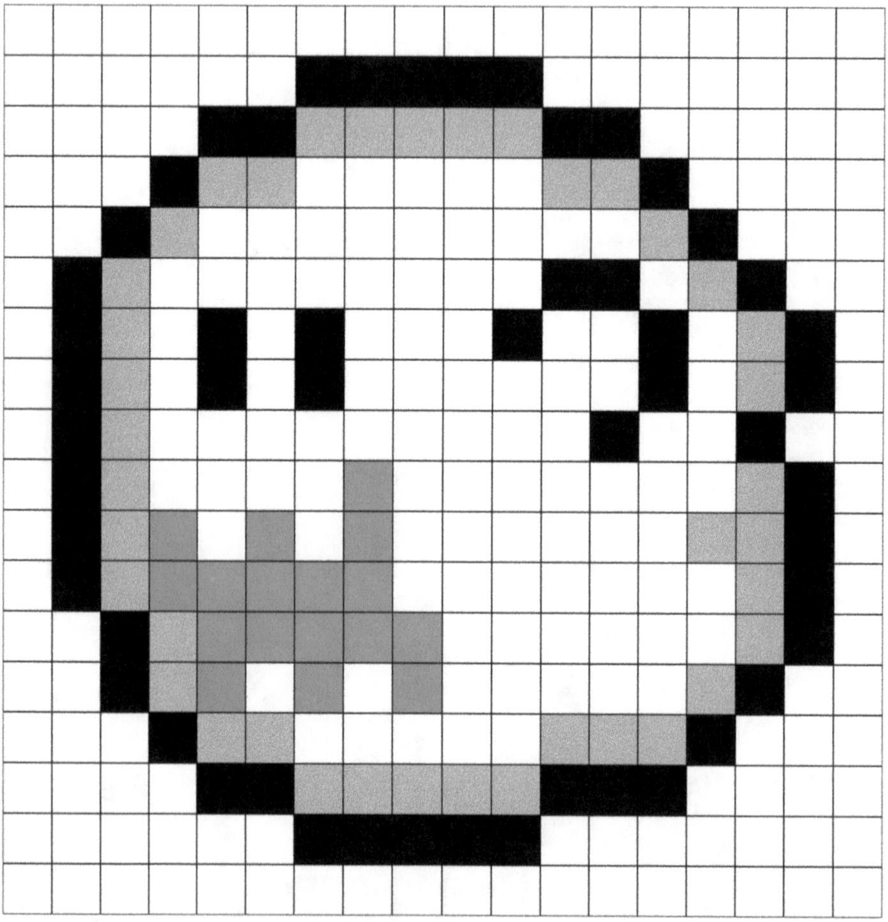

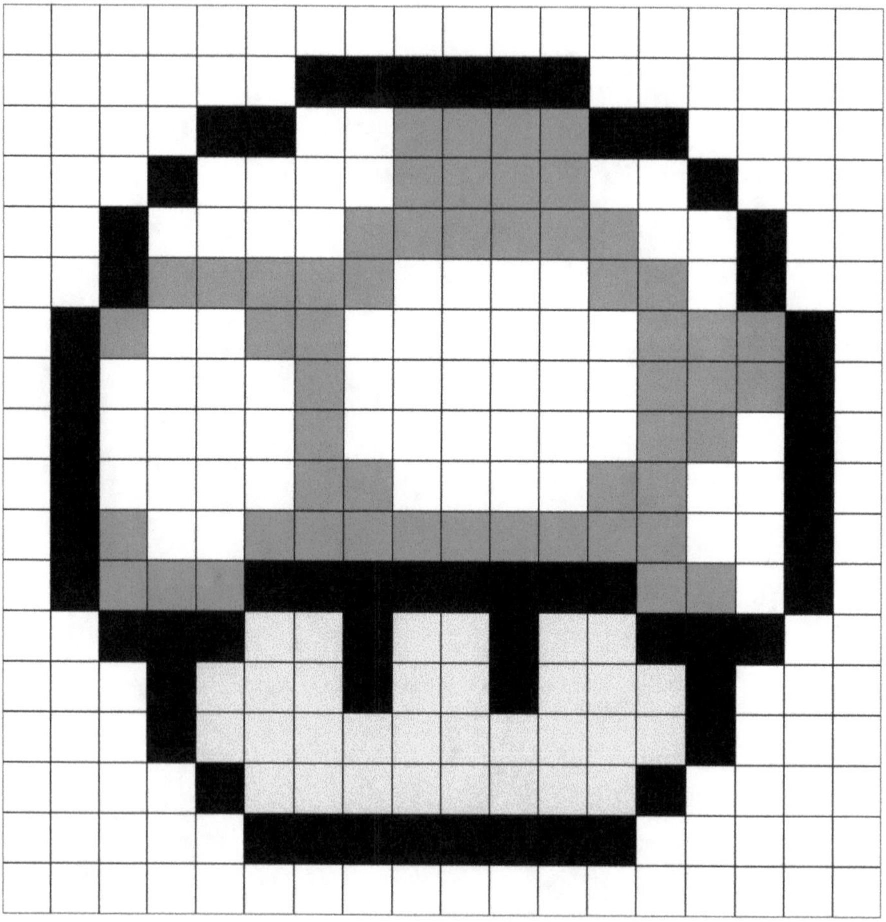

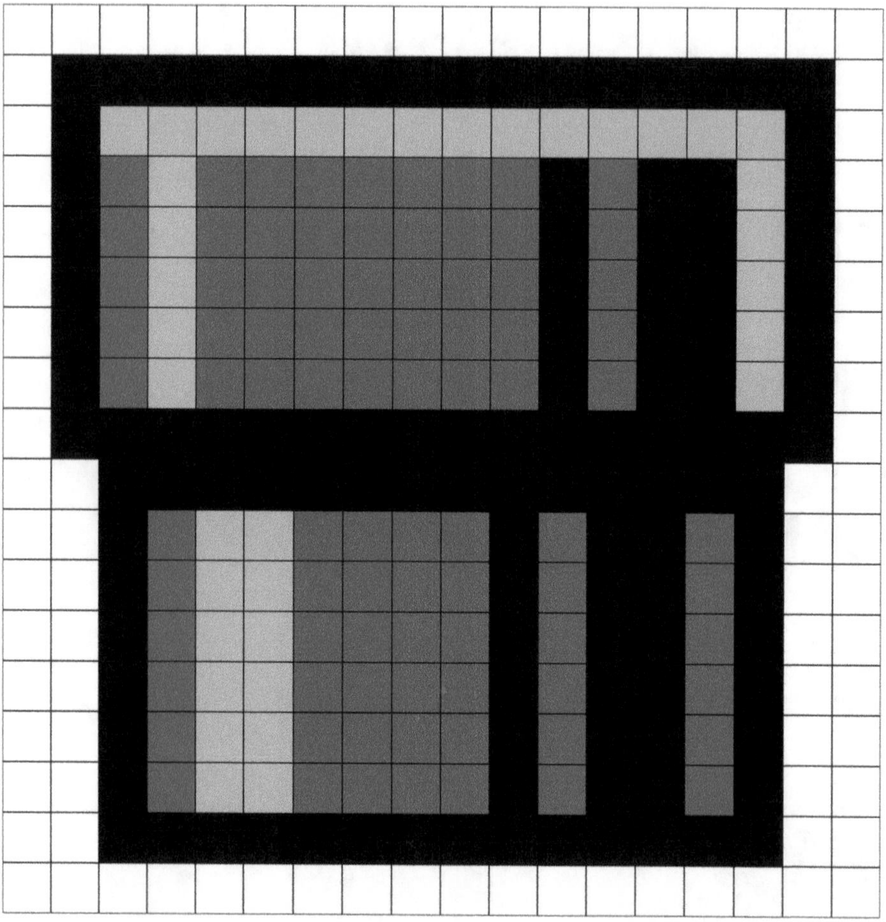

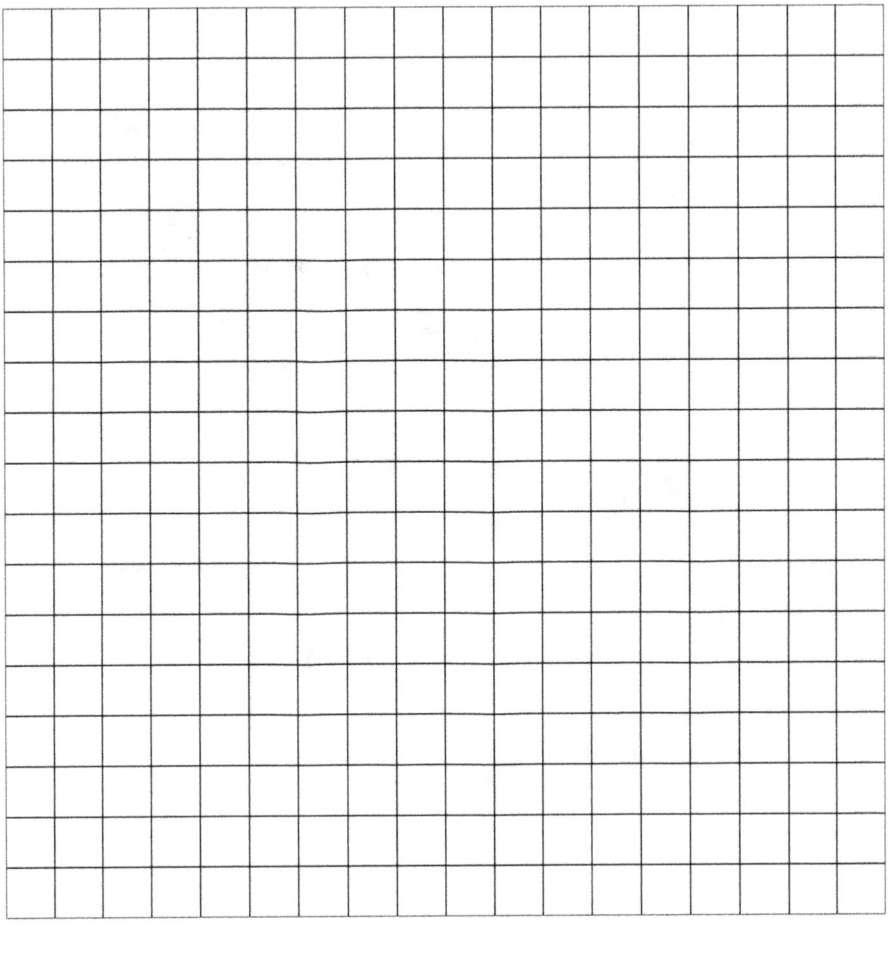

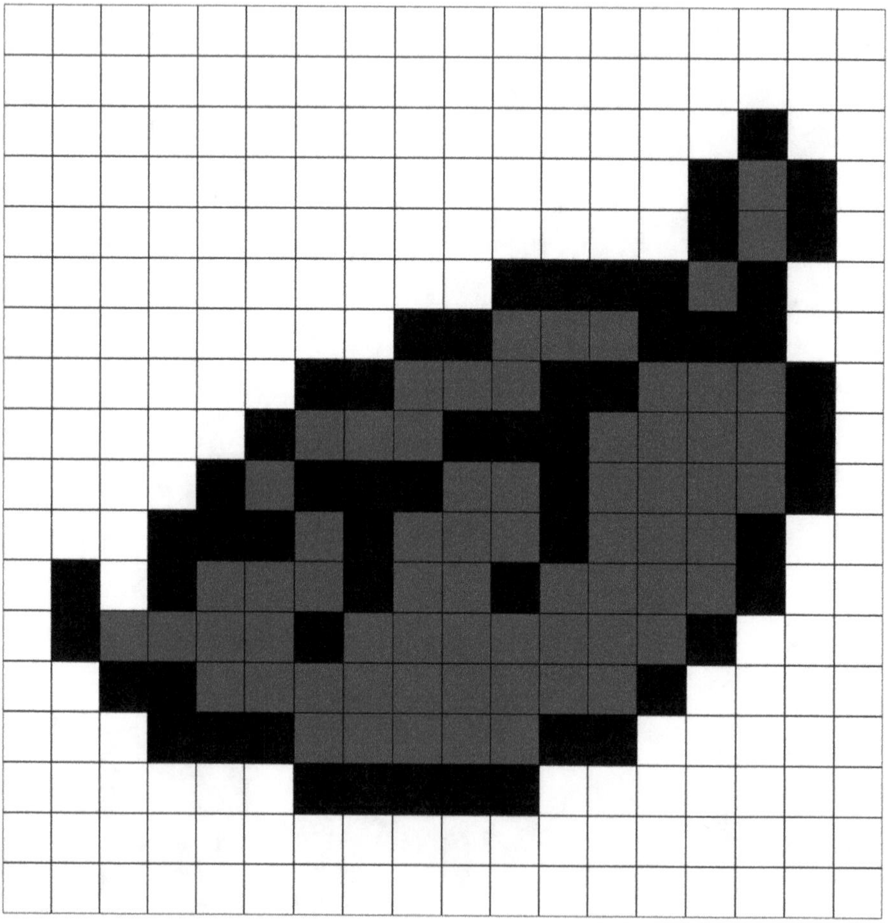

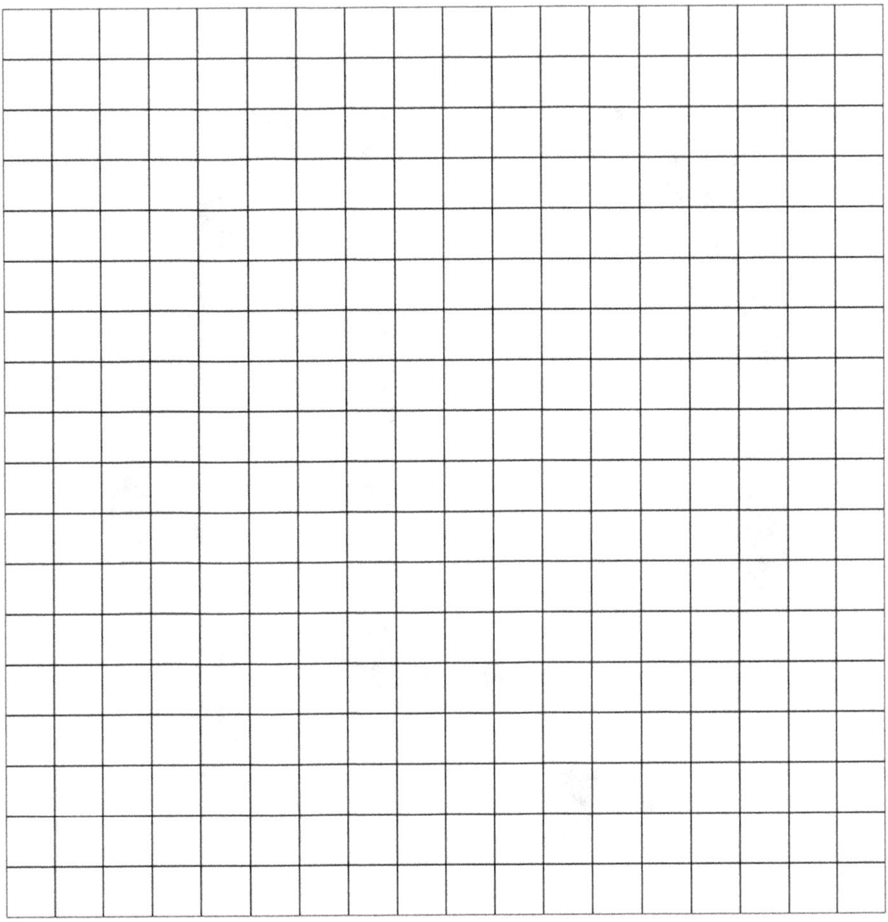

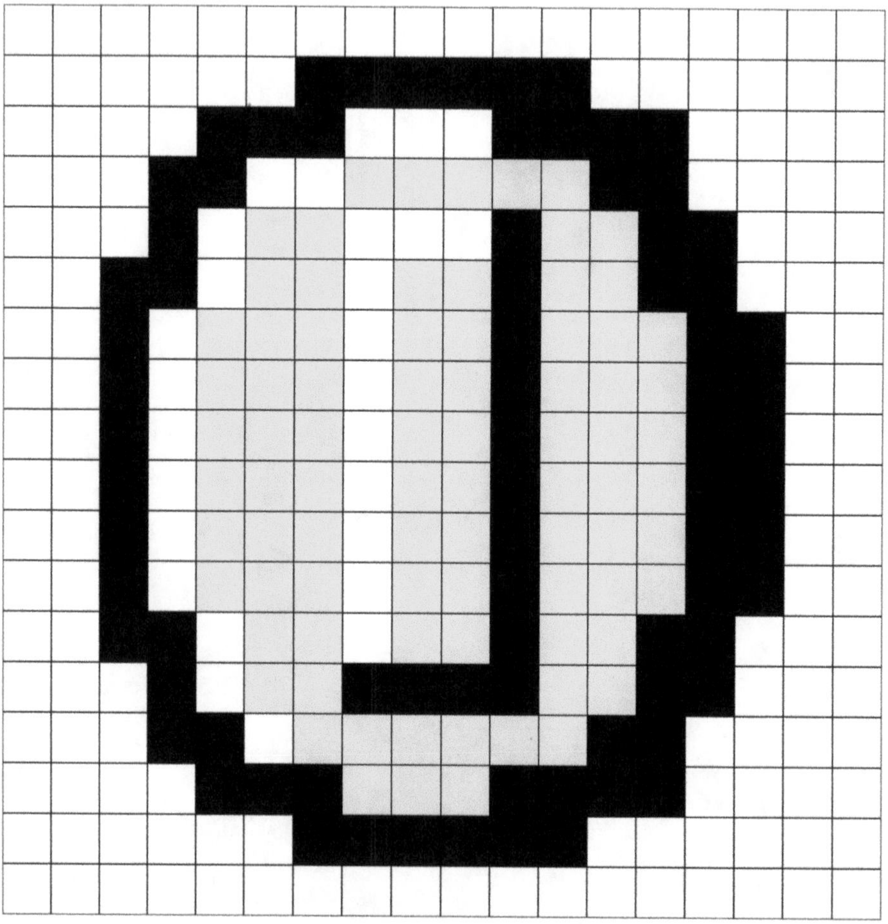

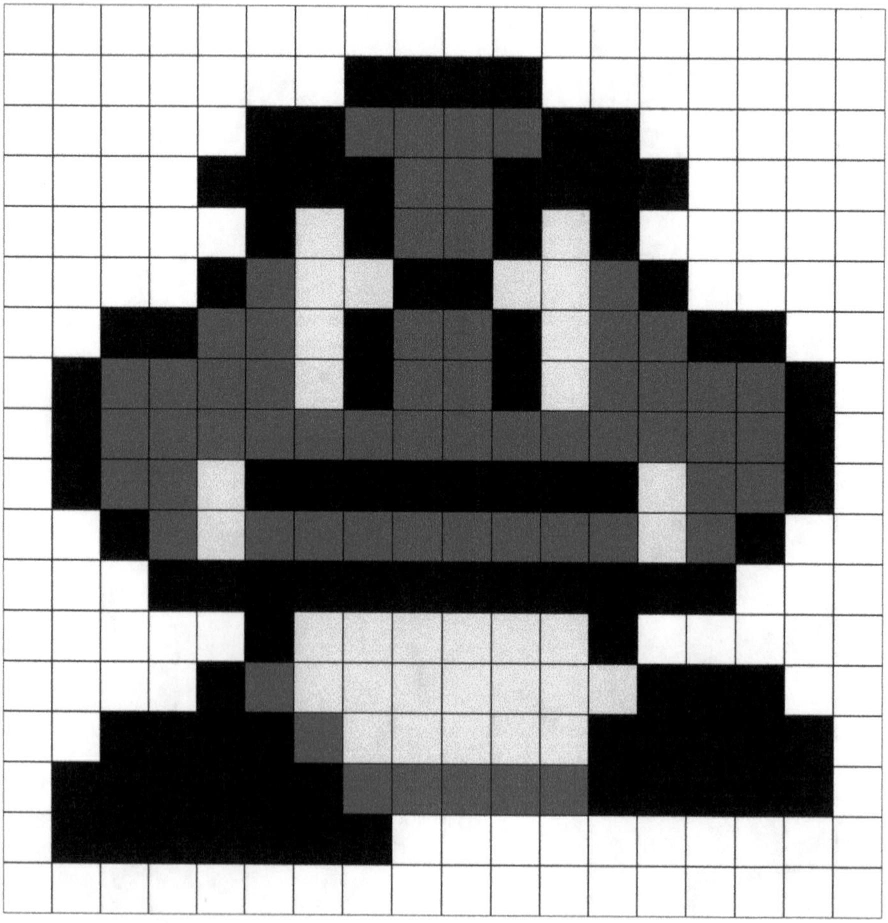

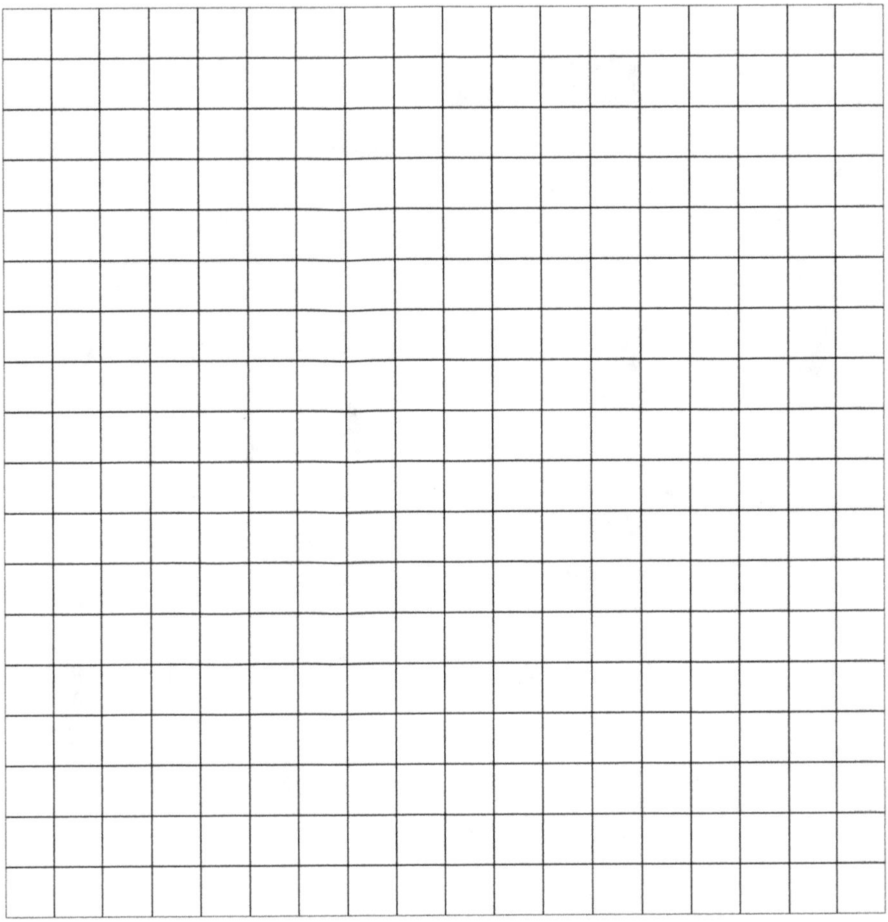

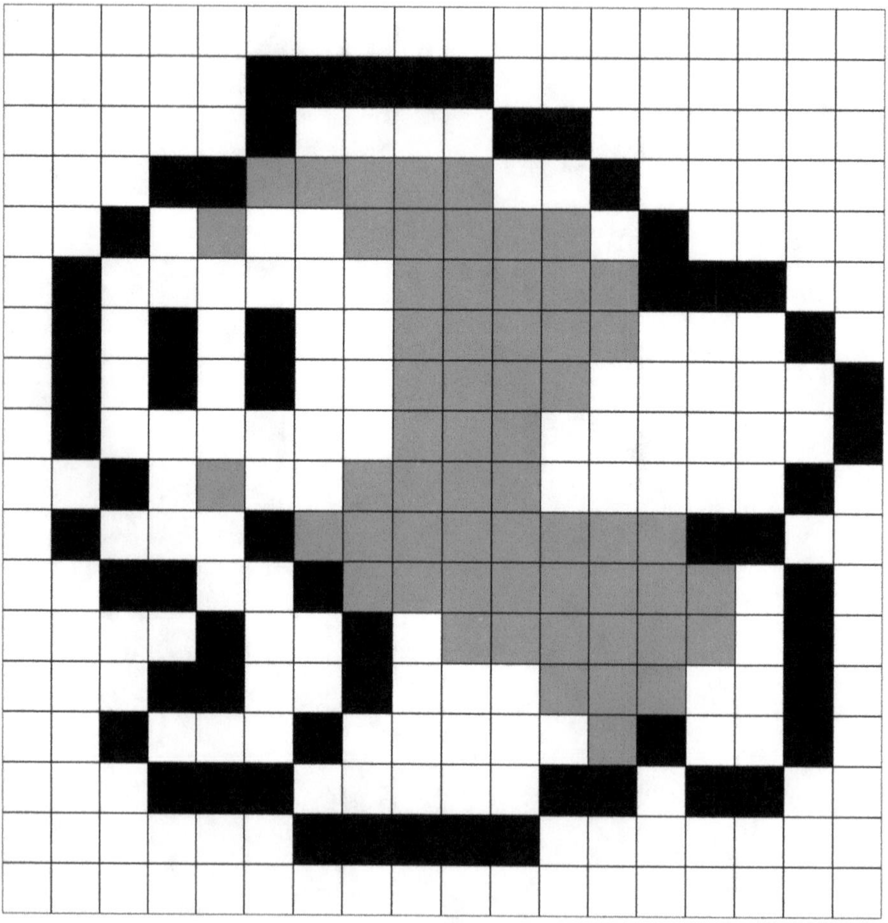

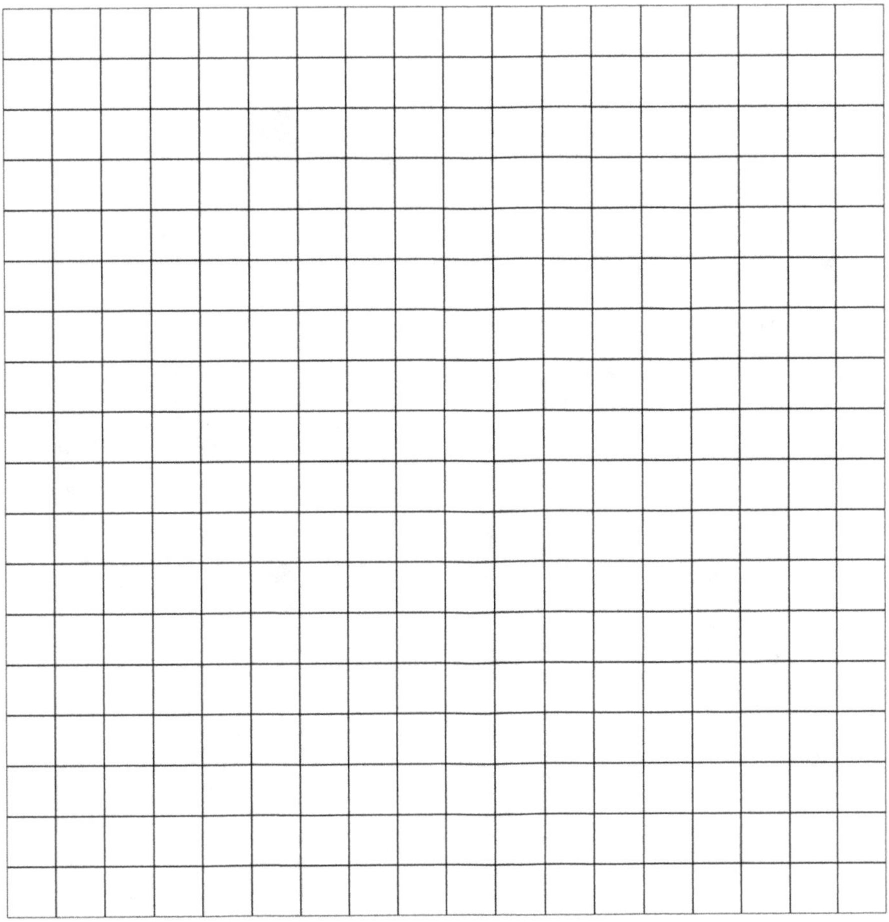

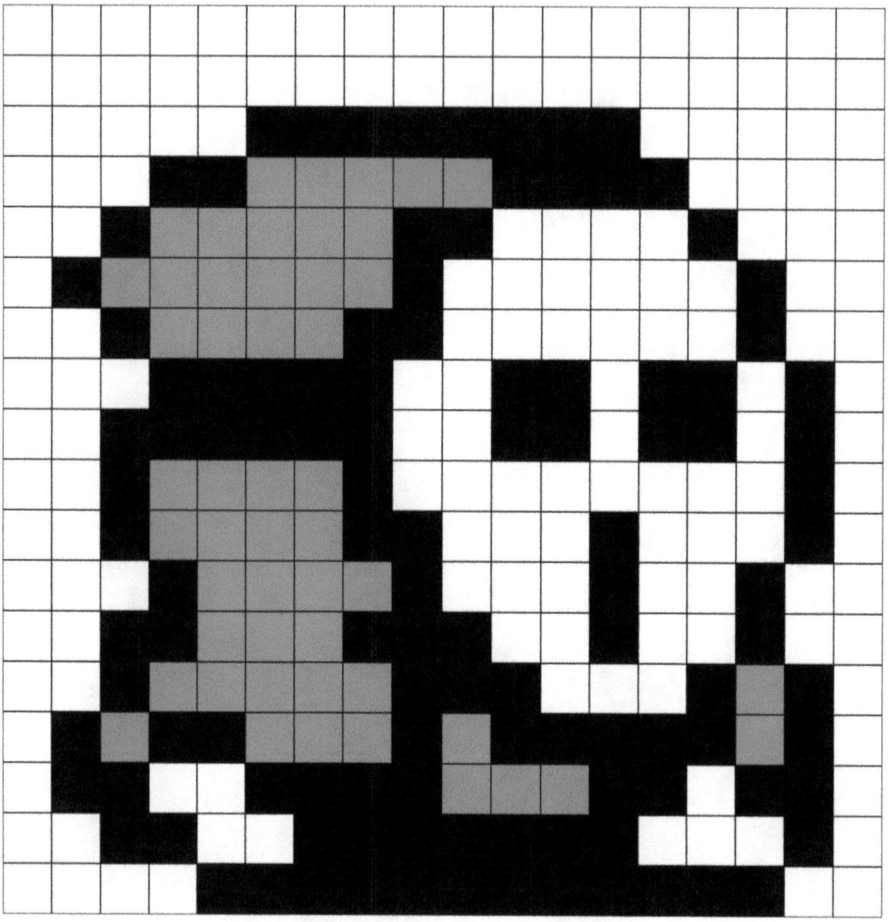

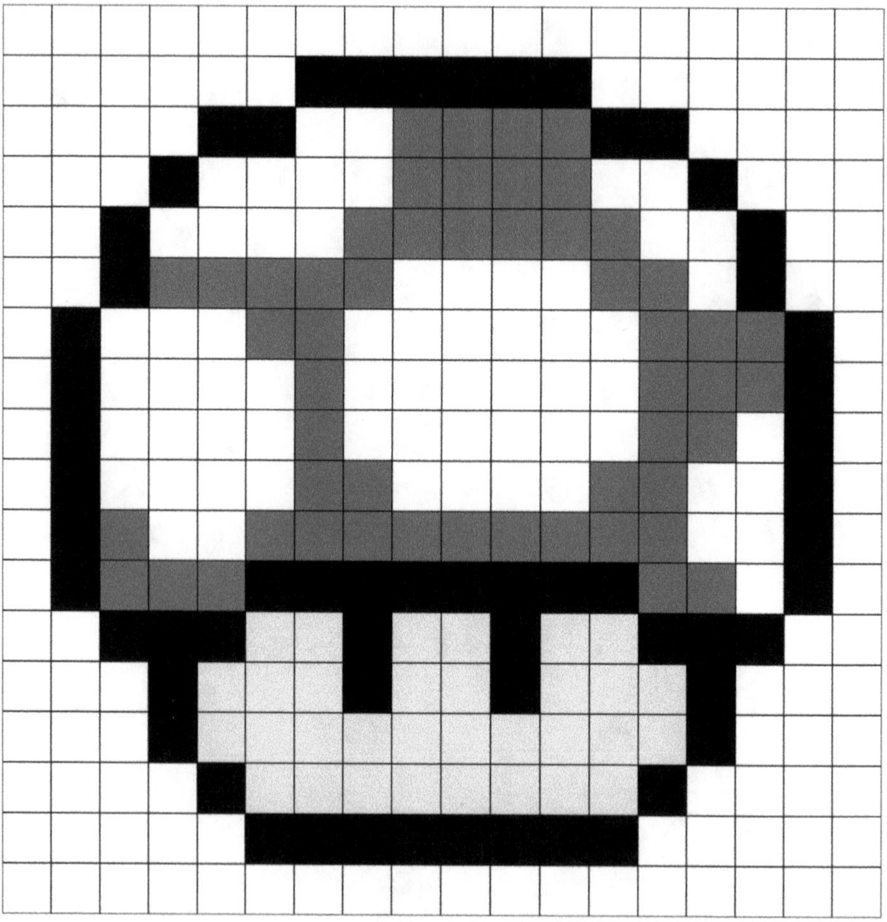

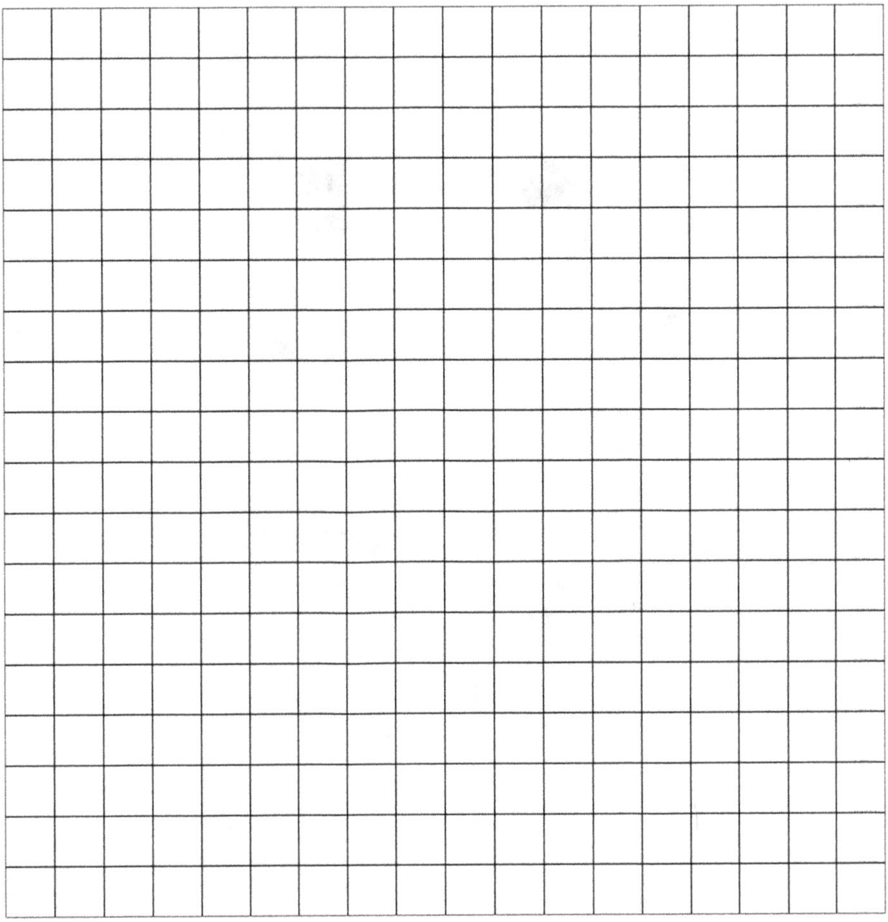

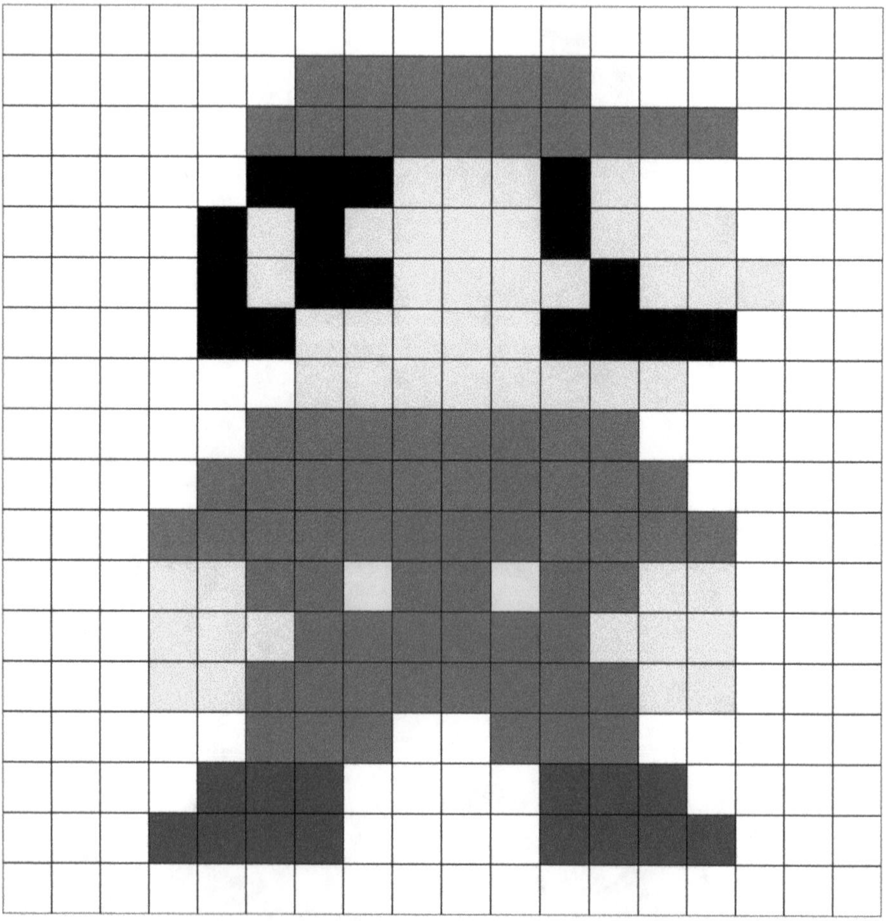

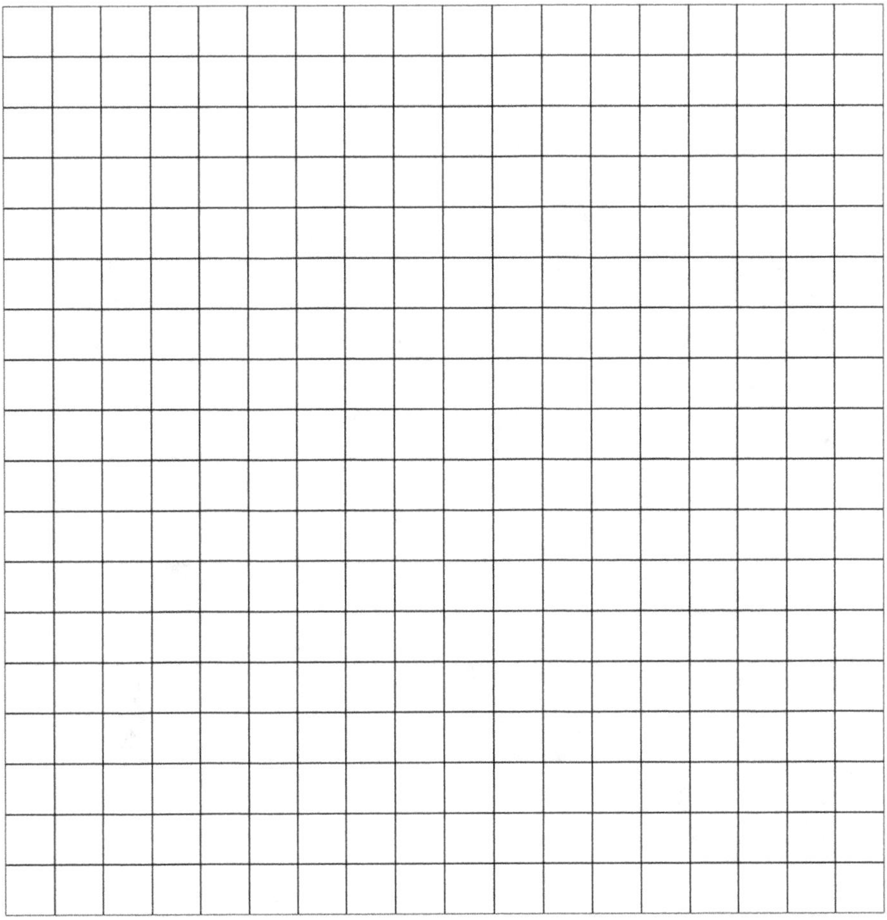

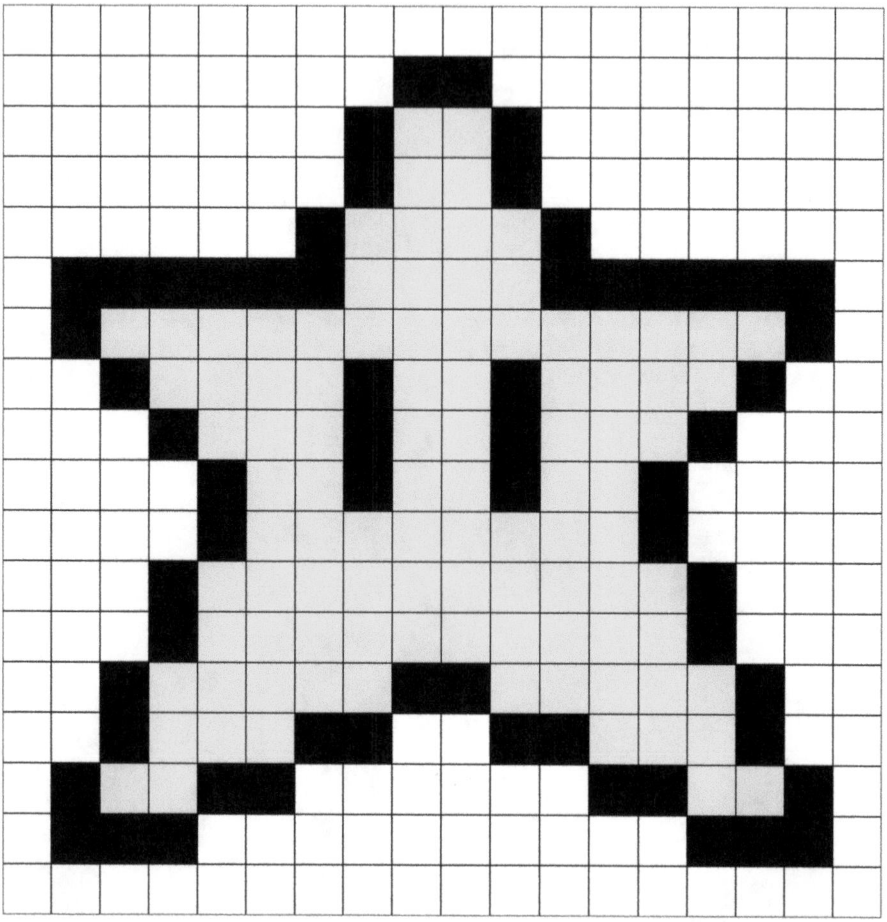

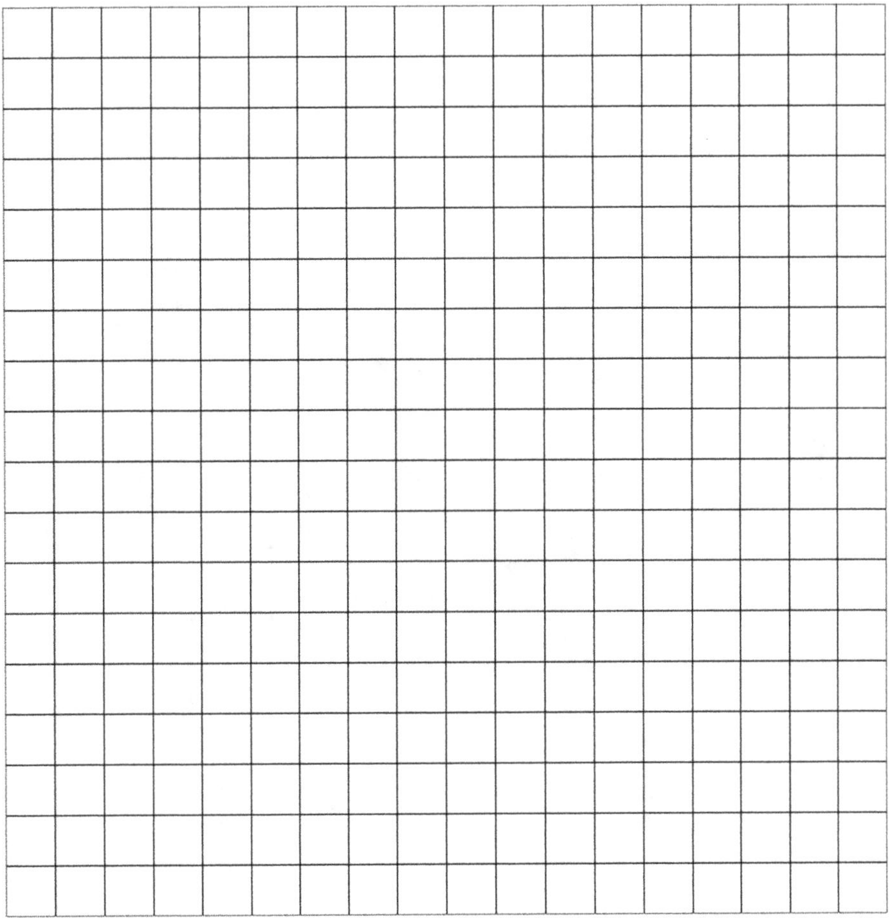

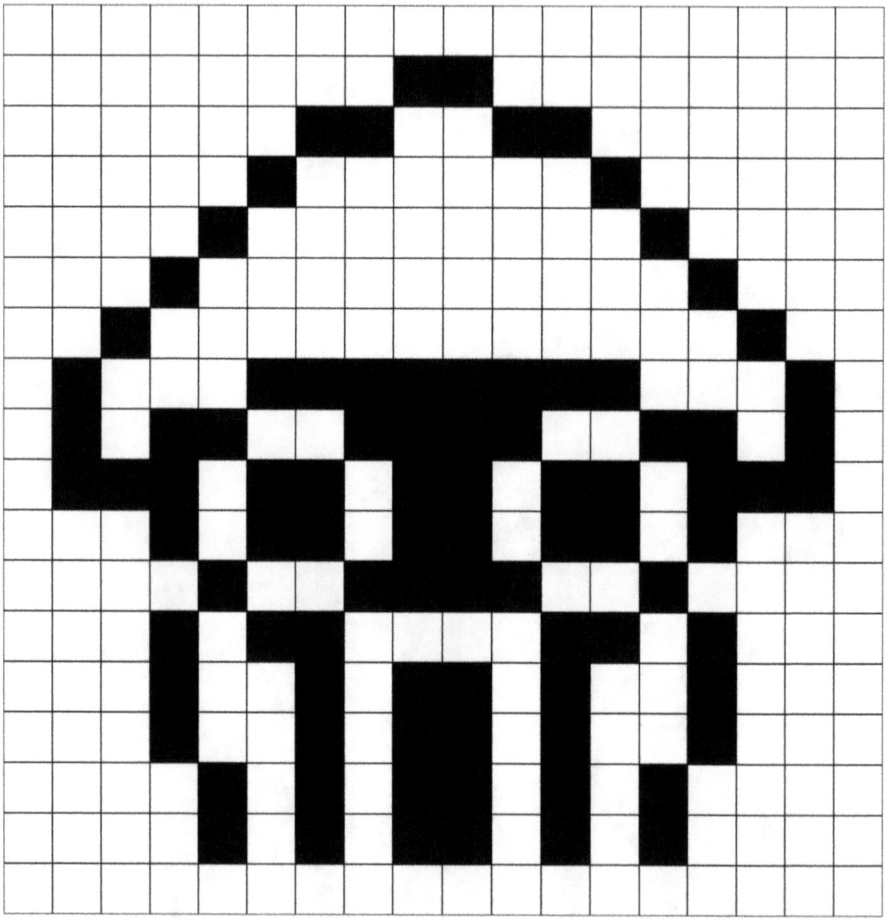

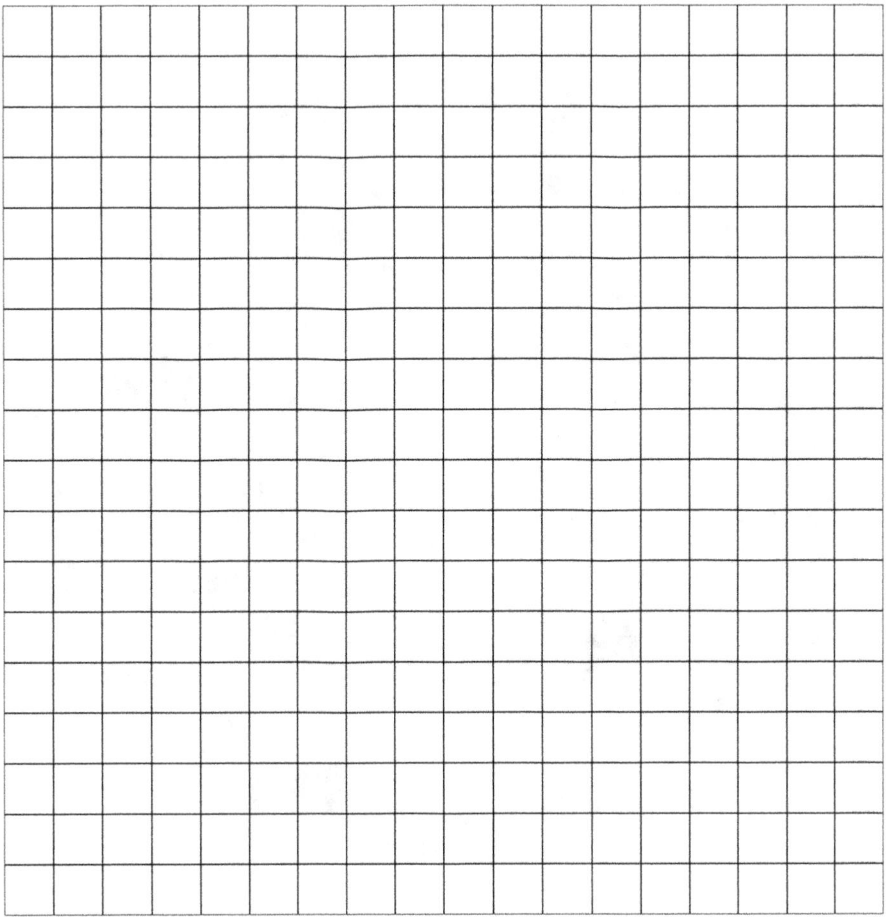

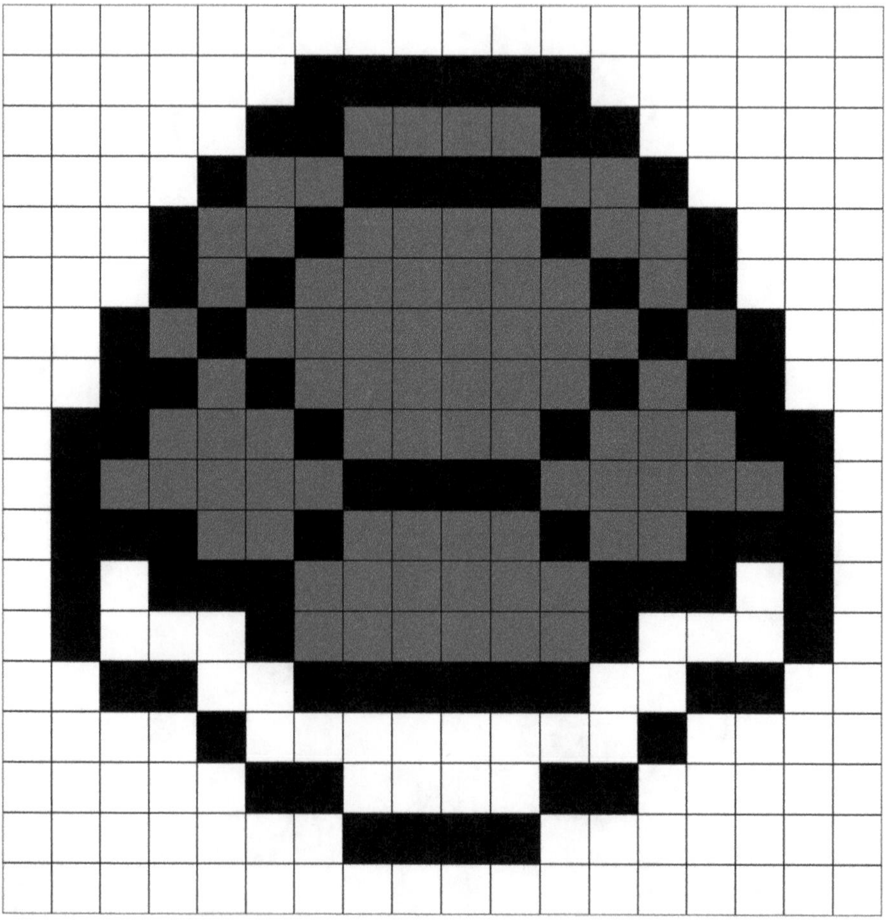

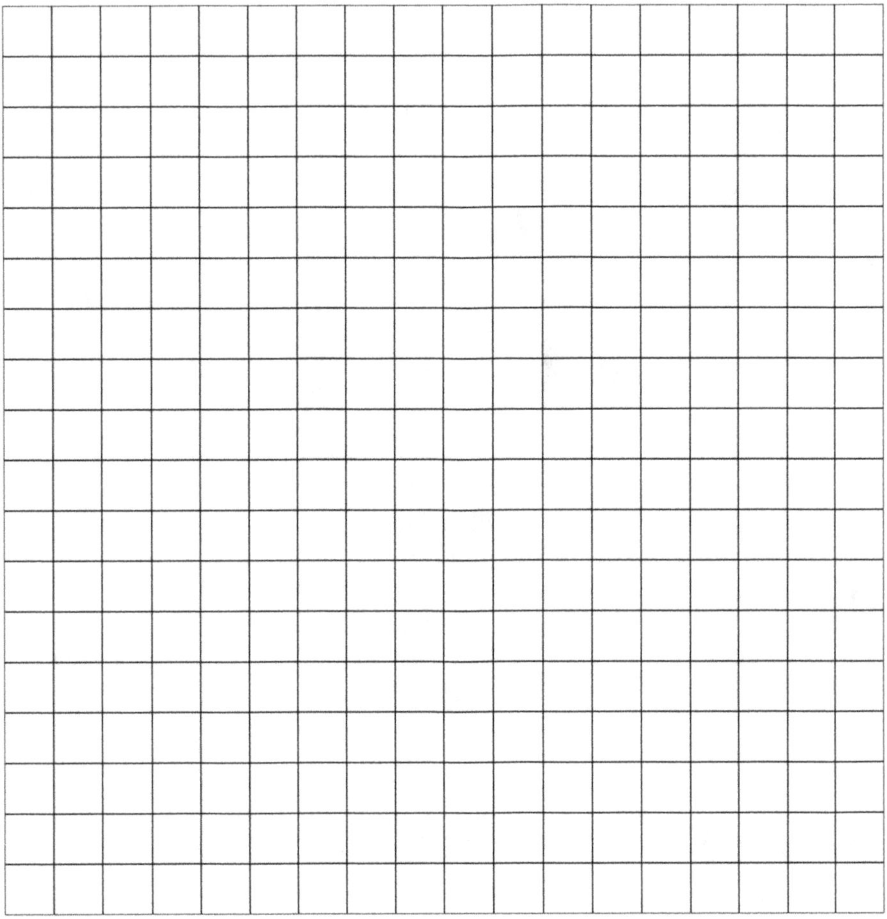

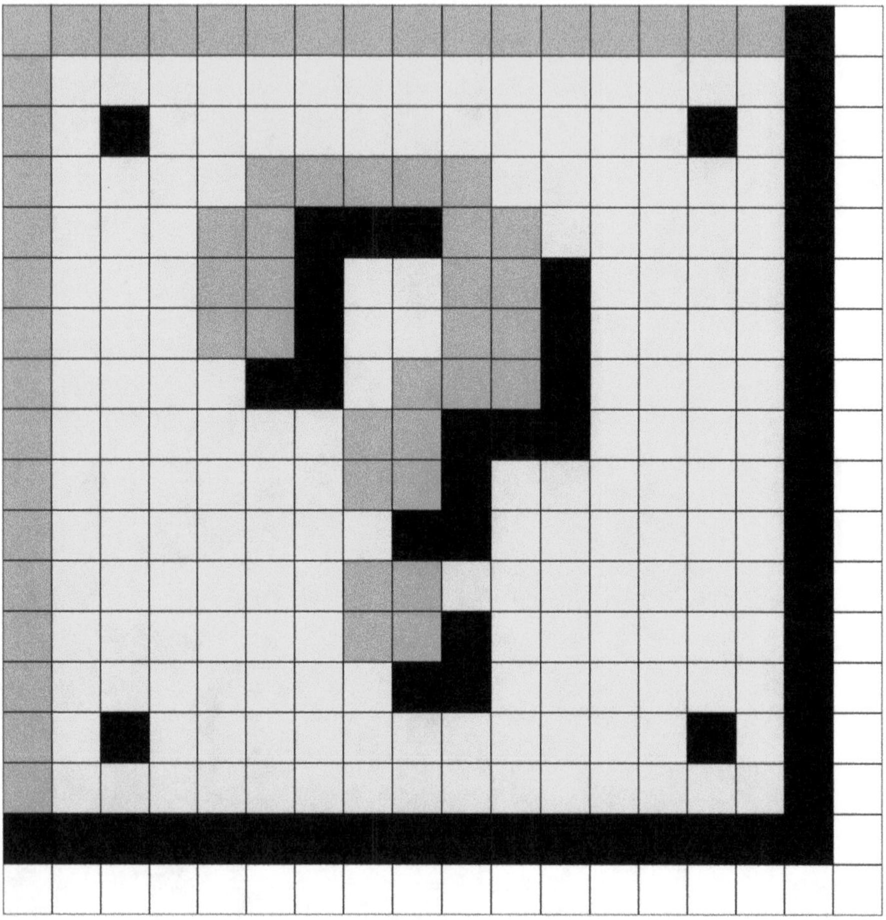

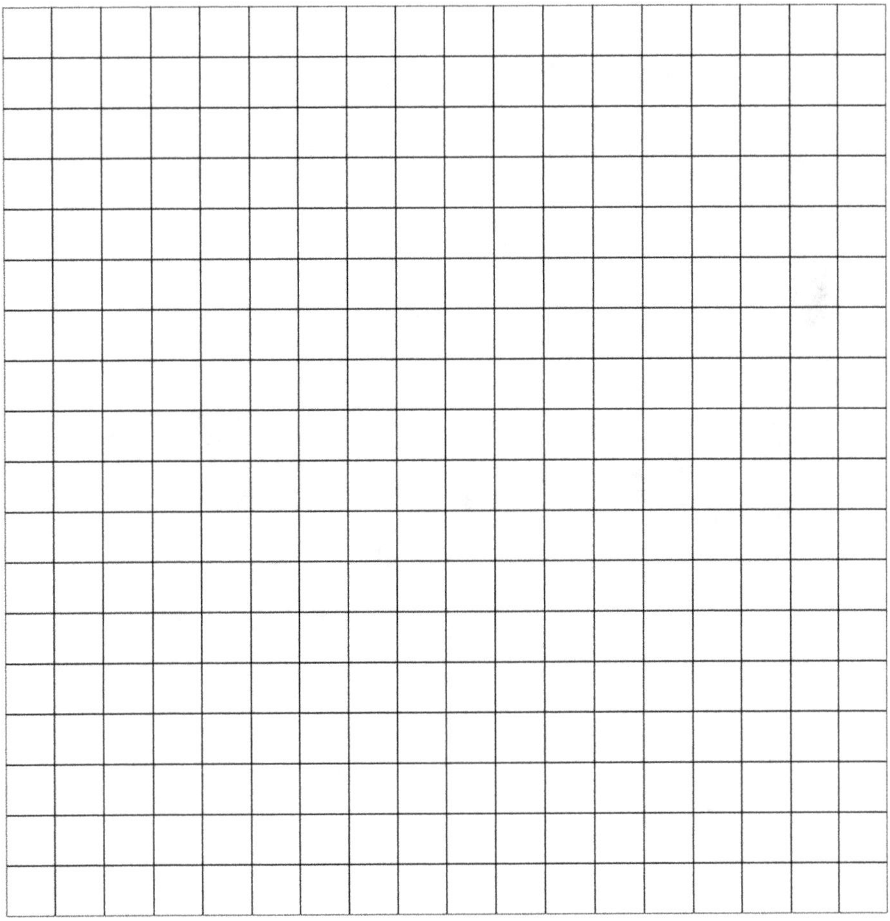

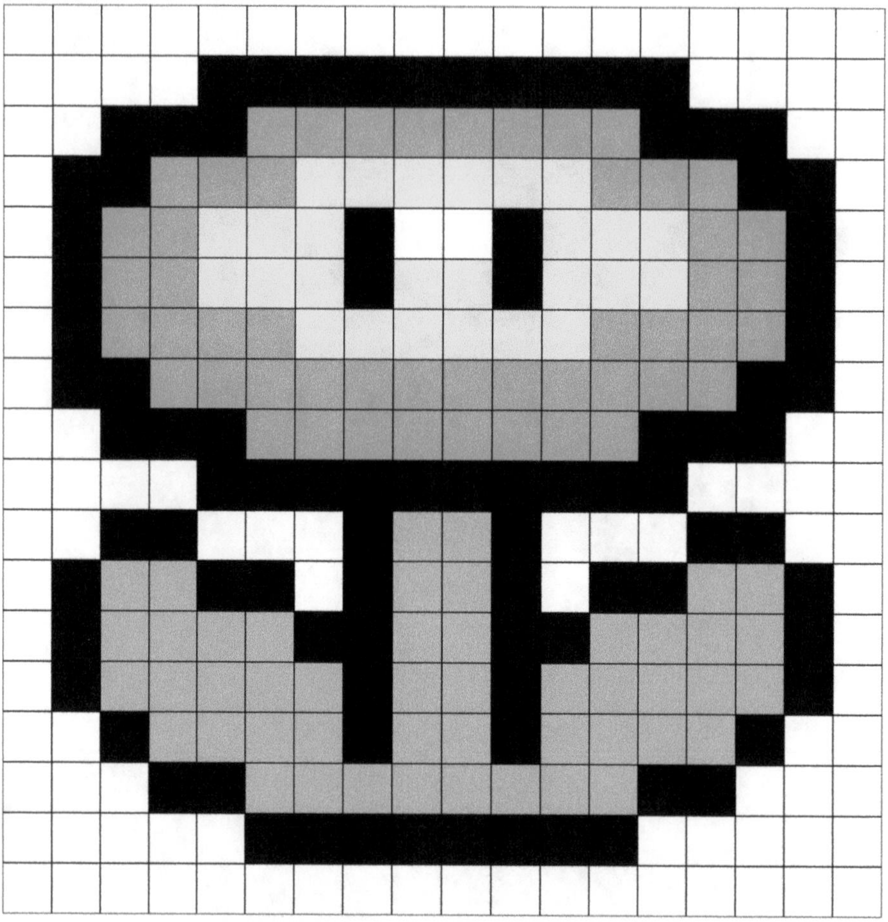

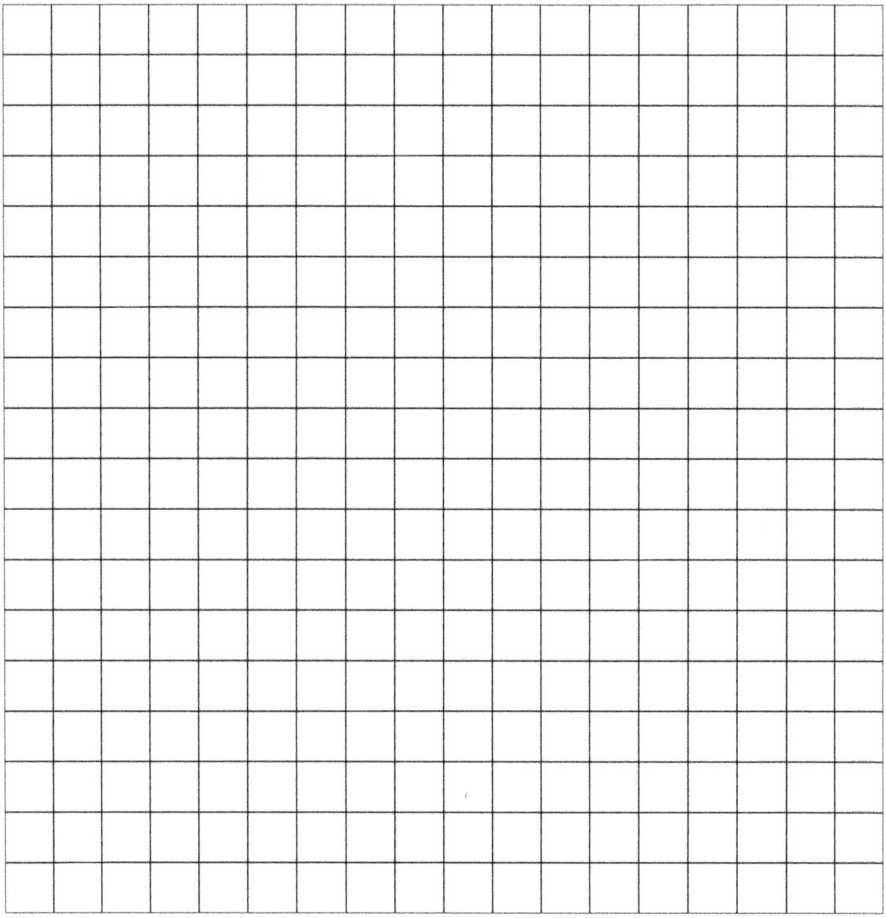

Printed in the USA
CPSIA information can be obtained
at www.ICGtesting.com
LVHW022243111123
763692LV00014B/905

9 789403 647609